America and Women

Fictionized Biography

MARJORIE R. LONGWELL

DORRANCE & COMPANY
Philadelphia

PREFACE

Pick up any American History and search through its index for mention of the names of women. You'll discover that historians have given practically all achievement credits to fathers, sons and husbands.

The mythical fellow from Mars on his first Earth visit might wander, perhaps, among the forest of marble statues in Statuary Hall in Washington, D.C., and receive the impression that this was a land of men. He'd suddenly spy Frances Willard's statue. "Look," he'd say to himself, "women must live here, too!"

Both men and women built America. And this book tries to give the sweep of American History as seen through the eyes of seven women who helped create for us our today.

Awareness of their contributions, familiarity with their biographies, should be cultural endowment of every loyal American. Acquiring such knowledge is an enjoyable task, for the lives of our important American women brim with drama.

Everyone loves a love story, and Anne Hutchinson's entire life was a story of love. We thrill to adventure, and adventure was the keynote of Margaret Brent's activities in Maryland. Few modern career women can match the success that Eliza Lucas Pinckney achieved as business woman, wife, mother, patriot.

Susan B. Anthony, who witnessed the War Between the States, fought and won a 53-year war of her own against traditional thinking. At the beginning of her crusade, almost no woman possessed a purse of her own; today millions of American women are self-supporting citizens. How many pause, even once a year on Susan B. Anthony's birthday, to remember the deep debt they owe this Quaker girl, who perhaps was America's greatest woman?

At the age of sixty, Mary Baker Eddy was unknown. At eighty-seven she conceived the idea of publishing a daily newspaper, sold today throughout the civilized world. In every civilized country, hundreds of churches, filled each Sunday to capacity, owe their very existence to this American woman, born in 1821 upon a New Hampshire farm.

The Negro girl, Maggie Lena Walker, arose to the position of our country's first woman Bank President. Every child who drops a penny into his small cardboard bank given to him by the Big Bank, pays tribute to the financial astuteness of Maggie Lena Walker, who first thought of this. No Horatio Alger hero ever made a more amazing climb from obscurity to wealth than did Maggie Lena Walker. Her only staff was her stout heart.

Emma Lazarus, the Jewish girl, lived and died in the nineteenth century, yet she press-agented today's Israel. She wrote about Israel. She raised money for it. Also, she wrote poetry. And she gave us a new conception of adult education.

I have tried, in writing these biographies, to emphasize the truth that today's America was created by men and women of all races, creeds, social standing. Emma Lazarus was a

Jewish girl, Margaret Brent, a Catholic. Eliza Lucas Pinckney was the daughter of a British army officer, and Maggie Lena Walker, the daughter of a Negro slave. Anne Hutchinson, Mary Baker Eddy, Susan B. Anthony, held divergent religious beliefs; yet all offered their gifts to a common cause. Each helped in her own way to make our country great and strong.

I give you seven outstanding Americans. May you enjoy meeting them!

ACKNOWLEDGMENTS

In Public Libraries of many United States cities, the Library of Congress, Huntington Library, even in the British Museum Library of London, England, I have searched for material for this book. I've visited the "home towns" of all seven women, and this helped make their stories come alive.

I've read many letters written in longhand by Eliza Lucas Pinckney and studied her published letters (Harriott Horrey Ravenel; Charles Scribner's Sons, 1896). Mrs. George C. Logan of the National Society of Colonial Dames of America in the State of South Carolina has been most helpful; and she obtained permission for me to quote three recipes from Eliza Lucas Pinckney's Receipt Book, published by the Colonial Dames of America.

As Secretary-Treasurer for years of the Susan B. Anthony Memorial Committee of California, I have read hundreds of Miss Anthony's original letters and talked with many women who knew and worked with her. Miss Susan B. Anthony's niece, the late Lucy Anthony, also her famous aunt's secretary, corresponded with me and gave me valuable data.

From Mr. Morris U. Schappes I received permission to

quote from his book, the *Letters of Emma Lazarus*, and Professor Ralph L. Rusk allowed me to quote from his *Letters to Emma Lazarus*, published by Columbia University, 1939. From Mr. Edward W. Forbes, President of the Emerson Association, Harvard University, I received permission to quote passages from Mr. Rusk's and Mr. Schrappes' edited Lazarus letters. The American Jewish Historical Society of New York City has sent me helpful material regarding Miss Lazarus, and also sent me her photograph.

Mr. William Pickens, Yale, 1904, helped me select Maggie Lena Walker for my book, and lent me the book, *Women Builders*, by Sadie Iola Daniel, also *Maggie L. Walker*, by Wendell P. Dabney. I talked with Maggie Lena Walker's granddaughter, Dr. Maggie L. Walker of Chicago, Illinois, about her grandmother and had an informative and interesting conversation in Richmond, Virginia, with Mrs. Hattie Walker.

CONTENTS

I

MARGARET BRENT
Gentleman of Maryland
(1601-1670)

The average 17th century Englishwoman, on reaching the age of thirty, asked little more by way of adventure than a fireside chair and knitting needles. Not so Margaret Brent! In 1637, shortly after her thirty-sixth birthday, she stood at the rail of a sister ship to the Mayflower to catch her first glimpse of Columbus' famous discovery.

Small and slim she was, with close-cropped red curls; and her long stiff black silk dress seemed scarcely on speaking terms with the little sailing vessel's shabby rigging. She stared at Maryland's shoreline, so lost in thought she almost forgot the existence of her brother and sister, also on this ship. She was dreaming of opportunity and power, freedom and dangerous living, in this fascinating, terrifying, utterly unknown new world.

"I hope Maryland Indians will know their place," said a voice at her side.

Margaret turned to her elder sister who, muffled in heavy coat, had dared at last to leave the stuffy cabin.

"Don't worry about Indians, Mary. Worry about the danger from our own Maryland white men."

Mary, pale from eight storm-tossed sailing weeks, gave her a startled look.

"Not physical danger, Mary. It's just that, because we're women, the men may try to keep us from living our own lives."

"If they did, you could toss your law books at them," said Mary.

The girls' laughter mingled with the twangy breeze that blew toward shore. Margaret"s law books, flinging about the cabin during storms, had caused much merriment. The Captain, in the interest of safety, had threatened to have the books stored in the hold, but Margaret argued him out of this. She couldn't spare the books, not even one.

Often when Mary's aching head forced her to lie in her berth, she'd watch Margaret who, seated on the swaying floor, an open law book on her knees, would be as oblivious to time and place as if she were reading in their spacious library at home in Gloucester, England.

"I learned from my law books that Maryland spinsters are forbidden to hold land in their own name for more than a few years, Mary."

Mary sighed. "So you signed *Margaret Brent, Gentleman,* to your Maryland documents! A fine signature to follow you through history."

Margaret patted a pocket of her dress. It contained a paper signed by Cecilius, Lord Baltimore, Absolute Lord of the Soil and Political Ruler of Maryland; and it directed his brother, Governor Calvert of Maryland, to grant Margaret "first-settler lands and privileges." Even if Margaret should marry, she would still own her own acres.

At that moment Giles Brent, the girls' brother, came running toward them. He stood at the rail between them and pointed excitedly to a small craft struggling over the waves toward their ship. It was propelled by several men with oars.

"That's Governor Calvert, coming to welcome us," cried Giles. "There he is, standing up and waving his plumed hat."

"He'd better be careful," said Mary. "Think how his elaborate cavalier costume would soak up water, if he should fall in."

Giles gave her a look.

"Don't be so practical, Mary," said Margaret. "The Governor won't fall overboard."

"Let's go below and meet him," said Giles.

Mary followed her brother, but Margaret lingered at the rail. What did the future hold for her, for all the Brents? Would Giles, astute business man that he was, plant tobacco acres and grow rich? Would Mary be allowed to worship God in her own devout Catholic way without interference? Would Margaret herself find independence here, and creative opportunity? The answers were all hidden by the years ahead.

She turned and went down to join Giles and her sister below deck.

Six months later, seated in a canoe behind a bronze Indian who was paddling her across the river to an Indian Settlement, Margaret watched the rise and fall of the man's powerful back muscles. He was lean and tall, with coarse straight black hair, and his only garment consisted of a deerskin loin cloth.

How well the Indians had kept their place, with the Brent sisters completely dependent upon them for help and advice! This man had taught them to make corn bread, plant potatoes and pumpkins, to hunt and fish. Once when Mary had a toothache, he'd brought her a root and told her to hold it in her mouth. The pain disappeared. Margaret wished he could understand more English, so that she might thank him adequately.

Today she was supposedly taking this trip to inspect yards of matting that Indian women were weaving for Cecilius, Lord Baltimore's home in England. In truth, she was coming to have a talk with Father White, priest of the Indian settlement, concerning rumors of dangerous activities of a certain man of her own race.

She trailed fingers over the canoe's edge in the cool clear water and watched waves dance in the sparkles tossed them by the bright sun. She felt at home in this beautiful land, and loved it.

Her feeling of security was due to Indian friendship, and this had roots in the wisdom of Governor Calvert, the younger brother of Cecilius, Lord Baltimore. Governor Calvert, on landing here with Maryland's first white settlers at the mouth of the Potomac River four years ago, had bought from the Pascataway Indians their entire village, complete with wigwams, acreage and planted corn. In exchange he'd given iron tools, silk and other commodities needed by the Indians. The new settlement he'd named St. Mary's.

A less intelligent leader might have taken the Pascataway Indian village with guns and clubs. Governor Calvert's business-like purchase had safeguarded St. Mary's young growing years from devastating Indian wars.

Governor Calvert, following his brother's instructions, had placed in the name of *Margaret Brent, Gentleman*, one thousand fertile Maryland acres. The two sisters had brought out from England nine colonists who had now built cabins for themselves on the Brent estate. The colonists would pay Margaret and Mary part of their every harvested crop. Margaret and Mary, in turn, would pay to Governor Calvert 400 pounds of wheat each year. Feudalism, transplanted to the New World.

Mary attended to details of the estate, leaving Margaret free to study her law books. Already, among St. Mary's 700 population, many men had come to Margaret for legal advice; and Giles Brent, during visits to his sisters' home, was often forced to listen to long discussions concerning boundaries, wills, the duties and rights of indentured servants and other local problems.

When alone with his sisters, he'd say sternly: "If you girls intend to marry, stop frightening the men away with legal talk."

"Frightening them away?" Mary's eyes would widen in surprise. "Why, men flock about this house like gulls about a ship."

It was true. Men came to talk of legal punishment for servants; and servants came to talk of legal escape from cruel masters. Owners of property came to discuss legal boundaries, and remained to speak of love.

Margaret treated all talk of love with nonchalance. Except that of handsome Thomas White. Just to be with Thomas White was happiness. She rode with him on horseback over rolling hills, down fertile valleys, through fragrant narrow wooded paths. Almost daily, he pleaded with her to marry him, but she was afraid that marriage might end her dreams of all she craved to accomplish here in Maryland.

This dream, which had lured her from an English mansion to Maryland's wilderness, had to do with bringing out shiploads of settlers and helping them to achieve, in this lush land, a prosperous and satisfying life. Every gain, she told herself, involved a corresponding loss. She could not have fulfillment of that dream, and marriage, too.

She thought of marriage as a full-time career in itself. She had no way of knowing that, three hundred years later, women would not be required to choose between career and marriage. They could have both.

And so she gave up the thought of marrying Thomas White, but she did not give up love. Love comes and is there. Thomas White's love for Margaret, like Maryland's sunshine, illuminated all her years ahead.

The canoe was close to shore now, and the Indian made shorter paddle strokes. He had cut down a gum tree, burned out its center with hot stones, and fashioned this canoe with his own hands. His manipulation of the little craft was skillful and sure, almost as if he and the canoe were one. He stepped from it into waist-deep water, swished it upon dry land, and then helped Margaret out.

As she walked through tall maples, she remembered what an early Maryland explorer had written in his diary: "Fine groves—choked with underbrush—trees growing at intervals as if planted by the hand of man."

Suddenly she came upon the Indian settlement with its noisy activity resembling a market place. Indian women, dressed in deerskin, their skirts bordered with colored beads, sat at looms on the ground, so intent upon their work that brown fingers scarcely paused in their weaving as the women greeted Margaret with friendly nods.

Men, squatted before wigwams, talked loudly to one another; and children ran about, playing a game with sticks and stones. The little girls wore doeskin skirts, the boys a breech cloth of brown leather. And as she walked toward the chapel, Margaret felt as if she were watching a world of make-believe.

The small chapel, built of split logs, reminded Margaret of a child's drawing of a house, with a cross on top. Its door stood open. Entering, she saw Father White, in long black robe, straightening on the wall a picture of one of the seven stations of the cross. He turned and smiled at her.

"It is good to see you, my daughter." He came toward her. "Shall we go out in my garden?"

She nodded and followed him outside to a walled area, colorful with flowers. The wall gave astonishing privacy.

"Father," she exclaimed, glancing about. "We're in England!"

He motioned her to sit beside him on a wooden bench. He said: "I've taught the Indians to make good brick, and they built this for me. My walled garden of meditation."

She glanced at the toil-soiled thin hands beneath the long sleeves of the black robe which engulfed rather than fitted his spare frame. Did he get enough to eat? But who could starve in this bountiful land with its waters teeming with fish and its sky often darkened with wild duck?

"I wish it were possible, Father, to shut out with such a wall all the world's wrongs."

"Shutting out wrongs would not help right them," he said. "And the cloistered life, my daughter, is not for you. Your brilliance in law, your courage, must help to make the world a better place."

She watched an oriole lift golden-yellow plumage against an azure sky. She said: "Father, I have plans. I hope to bring out a shipload of settlers who will create new homes on my acres. It will take years of work. I'll have no time for . . . marriage."

He smiled faintly. "With God's help, that decision must be your own to make. Marriage is not for all of us."

She felt peace invade her heart. There was such deep silence in the garden that a sudden rustle of breeze-blown leaves made a sound like a crackling fire.

"Father," she said. "I came to ask you about Claiborne.

It is rumored that he claims ownership of Kent Island, just off our shore."

The priest's eyes grew troubled. "Yes. Claiborne contends he had already established a fur trading post and settlement on Kent Island before King Charles I of England signed the Charter giving all land between the Potomac's south bank and the fortieth parallel to Lord Baltimore."

Margaret's heart beat quickly. Her legal mind admitted that if Claiborne had planted a settlement on the Island before King Charles' gift of all Maryland to Cecilius, Lord Baltimore, Claiborne might have a prior claim.

The priest said: "George, Lord Baltimore, father of Cecilius, actually did visit Maryland in 1629. Claiborne's post was not established until 1631. But it was not until June of 1632 that King Charles I signed the Charter giving Maryland to George, Lord Baltimore. Most unfortunately, George, Lord Baltimore, had died in April of that year. His son, Cecilius, Lord Baltimore, inherited the Charter; but you can see that it all makes for a legal tangle."

Margaret nodded. "And it is true, Father, that Claiborne speaks the language of the savage Susquehannocks and is training them to fight?"

"This I have heard, my daughter."

"And have you heard that Claiborne and his Puritan friend, Richard Ingle, plan to lead a rebellion against Governor Calvert?"

"Yes," said the priest. "However, just at present, both Claiborne and Ingle are in England."

Margaret sighed with relief. No need, then, to worry. At least not until their return.

"Father, what kind of man is Claiborne?"

"He comes of a good English family," the priest said. "He

was born in Westmoreland. Claiborne arrived in Virginia in 1621 as a land surveyor. He is now a member of the Virginia Council."

"If we might all sit around a table to discuss legal aspects of his claim, Father, we'd avoid much trouble and misunderstanding."

The priest nodded.

After a moment of silence, she mentioned the matting for Cecilius, Lord Baltimore, in England. Father White promised to see about it.

"Do you think that Cecilius, Lord Baltimore, will ever come out to his Colony, Father? If I owned this beautiful Maryland, I'd want to look at it."

The priest smiled. He made no comment.

Margaret knew that his time was rigidly scheduled. She stood up and said she must go. He followed her into the chapel where he blessed her, and they parted.

As she walked again through the settlement and down to where the Indian stood waiting for her beside the canoe, fear edged her thoughts. What would happen to Mary and herself, and to their settlers, if Claiborne should attack St. Mary's? Giles and Thomas White and all the other men would take up arms, of course.

When she was seated in the canoe behind the Indian's rhythmical paddling, the river's sparkling beauty did its best to quiet her fear. If war came, they'd all have to face it. They'd do their best, and leave the rest to God.

During the next seven years no further word came regarding Claiborne; and civilization crept like a tortoise into Maryland, with Margaret Brent helping to direct its slow tread.

She had brought from England a shipload of settlers, and

each had added acreage to the Brent sisters' estate. Now the sisters were the Colony's largest landholders. The settlers, after building their own cabins, had constructed for Margaret and Mary a large one-story home which the girls named the *Sisters' Freehold*.

The girls had planned every square foot of their new home, with its immense living room, several bedrooms, huge kitchen. Behind the house stood barns for storing tobacco, shed for candle-making, poultry houses, cow sheds, stables, and three comfortable cabins for the household servants. The immense cellar under the house would one day play an important role in Maryland's history.

Giles' tobacco fields were making him wealthy. He felt himself an important man in the community, and his concern for the marital status of his sisters increased day by day.

At the *Freehold* one afternoon he said to Margaret: "If you'd give more thought to romance, less to legal matters, you might some day have a home of your own."

"But I *have* a home of my own, Giles. And I'm quite happy."

"Happy? Without a husband?"

"Giles, dear, I'm eagerly anticipating the day when you'll consider me too old for marriage."

"If you do ever go to the altar, Margaret, you'll carry an armful of law books instead of roses." He looked at her intently. "Why don't you marry Thomas White?"

She flushed, and made no answer.

When Giles had gone, Thomas White came to take her to a meeting of the Maryland Assembly in St. Mary's Town Hall. As they rode, on horseback, she told him of her brother's unappreciated advice.

Thomas smiled. He was dark, lean and tall, strikingly hand-

some. His voice and gestures suggested a dominating personality, but his blue eyes were those of a dreamer. He said:
"Giles is young and self-made. It's said that a self-made man
tends to become opinionated."

"Speaking of self-made men, Thomas, wouldn't you agree
that George, the first Lord Baltimore, was a self-made man?"

"Decidedly. Wasn't he born plain George Calvert, in York-
shire, in 1580? Entered Trinity College at fourteen, graduated
at seventeen, then toured Europe where he met Sir Robert
Cecil, *a meeting that changed the course of his life.*"

Margaret said: "Often it's a meeting with another human
being that hands us the key to opportunity. Sir Robert Cecil
introduced George Calvert to King James I of England. And
the king took such a fancy to young George that he made
him Baron of Baltimore, and gifted him with all Maryland!"

"Yes," said Thomas White. "And it's interesting that Calvert became a Roman Catholic at the age of forty-four and
died eight years later, at fifty-two. He had packed so much
adventure and excitement into those years that his life story
resembles that of Ulysses."

"Yet his son, Cecilius, Lord Baltimore, will not even bother
to cross the Atlantic for a glimpse of Maryland," said Margaret. "Ironic, isn't it?"

Thomas nodded. "It illustrates one of life's greatest truths:
people are different."

Margaret agreed, and they rode on in thoughtful silence
toward Town Hall.

A short time later, seated as a spectator in Town Hall, she
watched Council members in elaborate cavalier dress, lace at
wrists, discuss and pass laws she'd helped them frame in legal
language at her home the night before.

As she sat listening to the voices of the legislators, she

wondered how it happened long ago, in the beginning of civilization, that women were not allowed to take an equal part with men in the affairs of the world. Here was a topic she'd discuss with Thomas White as they rode home.

But during their homeward ride, Thomas White's expressive face wore such a serious look that Margaret felt her nerves tighten with nameless fear. She'd seen an Indian enter Town Hall and speak in whispers with the legislators. What message had he brought?

Thomas said: "We've had word that Claiborne and Ingle have landed on Kent Island with many soldiers and quantities of ammunition, which they brought from England. They're training the Susquehannocks for an attack upon St. Mary's."

Margaret, seated straight and rigidly upon her horse, felt the reins in her hands tremble. The Susquehannocks had recently attacked 500 white settlers in Virginia, and had massacred men, women and children without mercy.

"Claiborne has spent the last few years in England demanding his Charter rights," Thomas White said. "But England's Commission of Plantations rendered its decision in favor of Cecilius, Lord Baltimore. The decision didn't satisfy Claiborne, and he intends to take matters into his own hands."

"How long could St. Mary's fort hold out against Claiborne and his Susquehannocks?" asked Margaret, her face deathly white.

Thomas made no answer.

When they reached the narrow dirt path leading from the main road to the *Sister's Freehold*, he said: "Tonight I'll bring Giles and Governor Calvert to your home where we can talk in privacy. We'll lay plans before calling an emergency meeting of the Assembly tomorrow."

She nodded, reining her horse to a stop beside his own.

"Margaret, these five miles between St. Marys and the *Freehold* will protect you. Thank God."

She did not speak, and he looked into her white face.

He said: "One thing is more dangerous to us than Claiborne and Ingle, or even the Susquehannocks. That is . . . fear itself."

She met his eyes. "You are right, Thomas. Fear is acceptance now of ultimate defeat, isn't it? Well, *we're not accepting it!*"

He reached out, caught her hand in his cool, steady fingers. Then he let her go. No, he would not come into the house now. He'd see her later that evening.

She watched him ride away. Then she turned her horse toward the *Freehold*. She'd have to break the news to Mary.

A few minutes later, seated at the long, wooden kitchen table, the Brent sisters tried to make plans. The *Freehold* cellar would afford safe storage for ammunition. Mary would care for the settlers' children, thus leaving their fathers and mothers free to fight. Both men and women would be needed, and only mothers of babies would be excused.

War! The talk of it sharpened their heartbeats. But as Margaret and Mary continued to discuss it, they felt, within their blood, the courage of their fighting ancestors.

Among settlers on the Brent estate would be men who'd served in England's army. They could train the other men. But this training must begin at once.

The girls talked until darkness fell, and Mary had to light the kitchen candles. A servant came to prepare dinner, but they dismissed her. They could not eat. And presently they heard the sound of distant hoofs.

They went into the living room where Mary lighted a long taper and applied its flame to many candles in the wall brackets. The room grew bright. She extinguished the taper with thumb and finger, then dropped it into its holder in a corner of the room.

A few moments later the men came in; Thomas White, Governor Calvert, Giles and a William Greene. Margaret remembered Giles had told her the Governor was fond of Mr. Greene and relied upon his judgment.

The Governor seated himself on the sofa with Mr. Greene beside him, while Giles took an easy chair. Thomas White pulled a straight chair close to Margaret's. Mary seated herself in a corner, part of the group, yet not perhaps an important member of it.

In the revealing light, the faces of the men betrayed their inner tensions. Margaret saw the Governor's colorless lips twitch nervously, and saw William Greene's fingers press against his cheeks as if to ease the paralyzing stiffness of his face. Giles was very pale. She glanced at Thomas White, whose blue eyes held deep concern for Mary and herself.

"Tomorrow at Assembly Meeting, I'll ask that money be set aside at once for war, and soldiers' uniforms," the Governor said.

"Why bother about uniforms?" asked Margaret. "The important thing is that every man and woman be pressed into military service, and trained."

She outlined the plans she and Mary had talked over, and the men listened with respect. The Governor agreed that the *Freehold's* cellar might be used for storing ammunition and guns.

They talked on and on into the night.

Next day the Assembly met and adopted resolutions made in the *Freehold's* living room. Every available man and woman in the Colony must take part in its defense.

And during the days that followed, all Maryland became a

war theatre. Men submitted to long hours of drill under the direction of those who had served in England's army. The younger, stronger women shared this training, and others performed farm chores. They chopped wood, plowed fields, did the cooking.

Then, one dark night, Claiborne and Ingle led an attack against St. Marys and captured it. An Indian runner brought the news to Margaret at the *Freehold*. Governor Calvert and William Greene had escaped and fled to Virginia; but Giles had been captured and placed in irons on one of Claiborne's ships.

"What of Thomas White?" asked Margaret, her heart beating in almost unbearable pain.

The Indian could not tell her. He did not know. Perhaps Thomas White had been killed by Claiborne, or by his men.

Margaret closed her eyes. When she was able to open them again, she asked the Indian whether the Susquehannocks had been fighting at the side of Claiborne and Ingle.

The Indian had not seen the Susquehannocks. However, he had heard . . .

She could not listen to his story. Incredible cruelty like this tore her heart, made her feel faint. She dismissed the Indian.

In the house, she found Mary and managed to tell her what had happened. Mary's fortitude was astonishing.

"We're five miles from St. Marys, Margaret. We have guns and ammunition. *Let us show Claiborne that this is our land!*"

Margaret went out to tell her settlers the news, and they displayed angry determination to defend their homes. The men set up targets for practice, and voluntarily increased their daily hours of training. The women begged for the hardest jobs; herding cattle, mending fences, clearing fields. One and all vowed solemnly that, come what may, they'd not desert their posts.

During moments of leisure, Margaret struggled with temptation to ride to St. Marys and try to learn news of Thomas White and Giles. She even saddled her favorite black mare and mounted it. On second thought, she jumped to the ground again. "My going would only let Claiborne know about the existence of *Sisters' Freehold* and endanger the lives of my settlers," she told the animal, running her hand along the horse's quivering flank. She removed the saddle and let the horse go.

Two days later, word came that Claiborne and Ingle had set fire to St. Marys and put to the torch the Town Hall and all its priceless records. The news was indeed tragic, and yet it meant that the enemy would not now learn that the one who'd signed: *"Margaret Brent, Gentleman"* owned the *Sisters' Freehold* and its surrounding acres.

An Indian came with news that Claiborne had anchored his ships off St. Marys' harbor, and that one ship, with Giles on board, had left for England. The Indian knew nothing of the whereabouts of Thomas White.

Months passed. Claiborne and Ingle did not approach the *Sisters' Freehold*. They were apparently unaware that it was there. Nothing had been learned of Thomas White, and Margaret clung to the hope that somehow he had managed to escape. Surely, though, he would have sent word to her.

The *Freehold* had developed into a self-sufficient small world in which the settlers grew their own food, made their own shoes and saddles and other leather goods. Women made soap, candles, cloth. Sugar and tea grew scarce, but no one complained.

Now the men went through their military drill during early morning hours, and spent the rest of the day working on the land. Margaret watched them at drill, and gave them deserved praise during target practice. The men deeply respected their small "General" in her black silk dress, with sunlight brightening her short red curls.

And then one evening at midnight, after Mary and Margaret had retired, Governor Calvert, William Greene and sixty other men arrived at the *Freehold*. All these months they had been in Virginia, training their men, and plotting St. Marys capture.

"Just let us sleep," Governor Calvert pleaded. "Tomorrow we'll talk."

Next morning Margaret proudly displayed her settler "troops" and Governor Calvert watched with astonished eyes while they performed military drill. He congratulated Margaret warmly.

"Mistress Brent, let me assure you, these men are soldiers!"

She thanked him. Yes, they had worked very hard. Every single day.

Two nights later, Governor Calvert and William Greene led his sixty men from Virginia, together with Margaret's well-trained settlers, in an attack upon St. Marys. Claiborne and Ingle and their men were taken completely by surprise and defeated. The two leaders fled in one of their ships, leaving all their other ships at Anchor in St. Marys harbor.

Governor Calvert inspected the ruined town, and determined to rebuild it at once. He thanked Margaret's settlers for their help in defeating Claiborne and Ingle, and solemnly promised them that as soon as there was money in the Treasury, they should be paid.

"I know that you have invested many, many daily hours in learning to be good soldiers," he told them. "And in my opinion, good soldiers are worthy of their hire."

The men cheered. They marched back, with light hearts, to their homes on the Brent sisters' estate.

The abandoned ships were searched, and in one of them was found a man in irons, unconscious from starvation. Governor Calvert knelt beside him, observing the bearded face, the long matted gray hair, the gaunt form. Suddenly, the man somehow looked familiar.

"Thomas White!" cried the Governor, grasping the thin hands in his own.

Thomas was carried on a stretcher to *Freehold*, and Mary and Margaret Brent welcomed him with tears of joy. But how starved he looked! How close to death! He had not yet regained consciousness, and Margaret's heart beat so quickly that she could not speak.

Mary ordered him carried to a bedroom, and she then sent for a settler's wife who was skilled in nursing. Margaret did not leave his bedside until he opened his eyes and recognized her, and smiled faintly. She took his hands and held them gently, feeling that this was suddenly the happiest moment of her life.

After weeks of good food and rest, Thomas began to look like his old self, except for the gray in his hair. Giles, returned from England, listened to the story of Thomas' confinement in irons on the ship. He complimented his sisters upon their care of Thomas White.

"I should have brought you a medal," he told them.

The girls laughed.

"Every day in irons must have seemed a year," Giles said to Thomas. "I was placed in irons when first bound for England. No one who hasn't felt irons would believe their torture. Did Claiborne and Ingle do that to you?"

"No," said Thomas. "I doubt they knew I'd been made prisoner. The night St. Marys was captured, I had fought with a ship's officer, and in revenge for the beating I gave him, he ordered me placed in irons in his cabin. That's where, months of starvation later, Governor Calvert found me."

"Well, it's all over, now," said Margaret. "St. Marys is being rebuilt, and Father White, in his Indian settlement, is alive and well. Let us hope that Maryland will settle down and stop making history."

"From now on," said Mary, "I'd like one day to be exactly like another. Uneventful. Secure. Safe."

Thomas laughed. "But, Mary, that's not life!"

"No," agreed Margaret. "You are right. It isn't. We can never be quite sure of what's around the corner. We can only learn to face tomorrow as we should; square-shouldered."

Giles looked at his sister. For once, he had no words.

A short time later, history again laid its finger on Maryland. Governor Calvert died. In his will, Margaret Brent was appointed his "sole executrix" and also "Maryland attorney" for his brother, Cecilius, Lord Baltimore. His will decreed that William Greene should be Maryland's Governor.

Thomas White was still living at the *Freehold* when Governor Calvert died, and after the will was read he said to Margaret: "William Greene will come here and consult you often. Wait and see. In time, people will say that you, Margaret, are the Governor of Maryland, not he."

"Oh, no," Margaret said.

"Oh, yes," said Thomas. "I need no crystal ball to be able to make that prediction."

During the next few weeks, Margaret worked very hard. She kept all the accounts for Cecilius, Lord Baltimore, of profits from his crops and livestock. She helped prepare briefs for lawsuits that took place among her settlers. She was available, night or day, when Governor Greene came to her with problems, and did her best to advise and help him. Indeed, the Governor came so often to *Freehold* for consultation that it began to be rumored that Mistress Margaret Brent, not William Greene, occupied the Governor's chair.

One afternoon Giles, White and Margaret were seated
about a roaring grate fire in the *Freehold's* living room.
Thomas was telling her she should not work so hard. She
was doing too much.

Margaret said: "Don't you think that all my work should
entitle me to a vote in the Assembly?"

Giles stared at her, "Are you crazy?"

"Why, Giles? You think I couldn't vote intelligently?"

"Of course you could," said Thomas White.

"Have you forgotten you're a woman?" asked Giles.

"Just a moment, Giles," said Thomas White. "Do you think
we should so vehemently proclaim male superiority? Is it such
a stupendous achievement to have been born a man?"

Giles flushed and was silent.

"Margaret," said Thomas White, "I think you have a case.
Go to the Assembly, *ask* for a vote. I only wish I had been
reinstated as a Member. I'd be on your side."

Margaret smiled her thanks.

And so, on January 21, 1648, Margaret Brent galloped her
horse over snowy roads to an Assembly meeting in the newly
built Town Hall. As she rode, she mentally planned what she
intended to say. Had the Assembly excused her from paying
taxes on the ground that she was a woman? Why, then, should
they excuse her from casting a ballot? What would the men
reply to that? But you're physically weaker than are men,
they'd argue. Yes, this she must admit. But did the act of
voting require physical strength?

She would carefully and logically answer the men's every
argument. In the end, could they possibly resist her plea?

Fate, listening to her thoughts, must have smiled. Margaret
Brent had no way of knowing that her logical arguments
would be heard in the land for almost three hundred years

before women were finally granted equal voting rights with men.

Now it happened that Governor William Greene had been informed in advance that Margaret Brent would that day come to ask for the privilege of being allowed to cast a ballot. Also, rumor had reached his ears that many people were saying that she, not Greene, was Maryland's Governor. He told himself the time had come to put Mistress Brent in her place.

He sat at the head of the long Council table, and glanced right and left into the faces of the Assemblymen.

"Gentlemen," he asked quietly, "do you believe a woman should vote?"

They answered as one man: "No!"

"Thank you, gentlemen. The Assembly is adjourned."

When Margaret stepped into the room fifteen minutes later, the Assembly members were standing in groups, laughing and talking, preparing to leave for home.

She walked to the Council table.

"The Assembly has adjourned for the day," Governor Greene informed her.

She stood very straight, and glanced from one familiar face to the other.

"Adjourned or not, gentlemen, I think you will hear me out."

And hear her they did. She spoke at length upon her right to the privilege of citizenship, and explained that she had earned that right.

"Gentlemen, I ask for *two* votes. One for myself, as landholder. Another as Attorney for Cecilius, Lord Baltimore."

The men stood silent. She looked again at each man in turn. Two or three flinched under her scrutiny. But none came to her defense.

"What is your answer, gentlemen?"

No one spoke.

Margaret, flushing, turned to Governor Greene. He avoided her glance.

"Well, then," she cried, "I protest all proceedings in this present Assembly unless I may be present and have a vote as aforesaid!"

She walked from the room.

Outside, the crisp air stung her eyes. She discovered she was trembling. She untied her horse and was about to mount when, in the far distance along the road she noticed a dark moving line. She waited while it moved closer. It was a line of marching men.

Why were they marching? What had happened? Her heart began to beat quickly, remembering Claiborne. Were men marching upon Town Hall? Why?

She led her horse across the road and stood beside it near some trees, patting the animal into quiet submission. The men drew closer and now she saw that they were her settlers. They massed in crescent formation at the foot of Town Hall steps, then stood in silence.

Suddenly the door of Town Hall opened and Governor Greene and the Assemblymen came out. Margaret read amazement in their faces as they stared at the gathered crowd. The lawmakers did not come down the steps.

A man stepped from the group of marchers.

"We have spent many months in military drill," he said to the Governor and the Assemblymen. "We fought Claiborne and recaptured St. Marys. *We have not been paid, as promised.*"

Governor Greene's voice betrayed his nervousness. "You men will get your money . . ."

A roar went up from the men.

"No more words!"

"We demand action!"

"Pay us, or . . . we know a man who will!"

Margaret watched the Governor's face go deathly white. An Assemblyman touched his arm and whispered to him; and the Governor glanced in Margaret Brent's direction. He motioned to her.

"Would you come here, Mistress Brent, and speak to these men?"

She mounted her horse, rode toward the group of settlers, then reined to a stop before them.

Every man removed his hat.

"Your demands," she said, "are right and just. I shall sell Cecilius, Lord Baltimore's cattle, also the tobacco in my barns. *With this money you shall all be paid.*"

"Hear! Hear!" shouted the settlers.

"We believe you, Mistress Brent. We'll take *your* word!"

She glanced from one face to the other of these men who'd fought bravely against Claiborne. They seemed to sense that they possessed her respect and love.

Silently, they replaced their hats and fell in line. At a signal from their leader, they marched off in military fashion down the snowy road.

The Assemblymen and Governor Greene descended the Town Hall steps and stood about Margaret's horse. The Governor patted the animal's head.

"Well done, Mistress Brent," the Governor said, his face still white.

The others echoed his words.

"We want no more to do wtih Claiborne," the Governor added. "But if those men had not listened to you, who knows what might have happened?"

"With our Treasury empty, your idea of selling My Lord

Baltimore's cattle was an inspiration," one Assemblyman said. "Thank you, Mistress Brent. Thank you."

The others assured her she had saved the day.

She acknowledged their thanks. But she could not help remembering their silence, so short a time ago, when she had asked for voting privileges. Touching her horse with the reins, she galloped down the road toward the *Freehold* where Thomas White would be waiting to hear the news.

A few weeks later, Margaret paid the settlers and thus placed Maryland forever beyond Claiborne's reach. With money in their pockets, the settlers gave themselves wholeheartedly to the Spring planting and worked with new enthusiasm.

Giles did not approve of the transaction. He had not been at Assembly meeting the day the men had marched upon Town Hall.

"What kind of soldiers would demand pay for defending their own homes, Margaret?"

She looked at her brother. "A soldier is worthy of his hire. And Governor Calvert had given those men his solemn promise."

"Governor Calvert wasn't the owner of Maryland, Margaret. Cecilius, Lord Baltimore, may not be pleased to learn of the sale of his cattle."

"I've written to him explaining everything, Giles. I've asked him to come to Maryland to see conditions for himself."

"If he doesn't want to come, he won't," said Giles. "And you, my girl, may discover that you've been a bit high-handed in all this."

Margaret looked at him. She made no comment.

When Giles had gone, she repeated the conversation to Thomas White.

"Suppose, Thomas, that Cecilius, Lord Baltimore, *doesn't* approve?"

"Well," said Thomas, "what can he do? The cattle have been sold, the men have been paid. Besides, you sold your own tobacco and that money found its way into the settlers' pockets. This should prove to My Lord Baltimore that you had no selfish motive."

"Thank you, Thomas, for being on my side." She smiled, then added: "How I shall miss you when you go to visit your elderly brother in England! I wish you didn't have to go, yet I know you must."

"Marry me and come along, Margaret. When we get back to Maryland all this fuss about payment of the settlers will have blown over." He came closer, and took her hand. "I *believe* I've told you that I love you."

"Yes. You've told me at least once a day, since your imprisonment on the ship."

"Tired? You're tired of hearing it?" Color mounted in her expressive face. "Oh, no. Always, the words sound new and shining, as if they'd just been coined."

Mary came into the room to say that dinner was ready and that cook had made Thomas' favorite dish; partridge, with rice.

A month later, Thomas sailed for England alone.

At the *Freehold*, life went on, but Margaret missed Thomas White more than she'd thought possible. A dozen times a day she wanted to ask his opinion about this or that. And although she filled her daily hours with many tasks and duties, time passed slowly, without him.

One afternoon Giles came with news.

"I was right, Margaret. My Lord Baltimore has vigorously protested to Governor Greene about the sale of his cattle.

You've been ordered to appear tomorrow before the Assembly in Town Hall." He handed her a paper. "Here's your summons."

She took the document and read it. "Why didn't Cecilius, Lord Baltimore, send his protest directly to *me?*"

"Who knows why?" said Giles. "No one really understands My Lord Baltimore."

"I've avoided Assembly meetings since I was denied a vote," she said. "But I'll go tomorrow."

"Of course you will, Margaret. No one ignores a summons." His tone softened. "Don't worry too much. You were only trying to save Maryland for My Lord Baltimore."

Her eyes widened. Giles was actually defending her!

But next afternoon when she tied her horse to a post outside Town Hall, her heart held a new fear. How would the Assemblymen react to Cecilius, Lord Baltimore's protest? She felt reluctant to go in.

She glanced at newly built but lawful stocks, pillory, whipping post, a short distance from the building. Were they eager to receive a woman victim? She half smiled at the thought.

Then, squaring her shoulders, she walked into Town Hall.

At the long Council table the Assemblymen sat quietly, apparently waiting for her. Governor Greene arose, offering her the empty chair at his right.

As she sat down, there was complete silence at the table and among the many spectators seated nearby. Giles was at the table. She glanced at him, but he would not meet her eyes.

Governor Greene, resuming his seat, spoke in a solemn tone: "Mistress Brent, are you aware of My Lord Baltimore's written protest to this Council regarding your sale of his cattle?"

She felt hot color stain her cheeks. "I have not read the

protest," she said. "But I have been informed that Cecilius, Lord Baltimore has written to you."

The Governor picked up a paper from the table. He said: "I have here a copy of our reply to My Lord Baltimore. The original is already on its way to him and has been signed by every member of the Maryland Assembly."

Margaret leaned forward, trying to read the paper.

She said: "I should like to know, sir, what has been written."

Governor Greene laid down the paper and turned to her. He spoke slowly and with feeling: "Our reply states that Mistress Margaret Brent, by selling the aforesaid cattle and using the monies from their sale, as well as her own monies, satisfied the demands of our soldiers and *actually saved the Colony*. Our reply further states that without your prompt action, the enemy might once more have taken over Maryland."

The Governor stopped speaking, and no one moved. Margaret sat very still, her hands tense in her lap, as the true meaning of the Governor's words flooded her heart. She tried to fight back tears.

And suddenly the spectators broke into wild applause.

"God bless you, Mistress Brent!"

"You saved our Colony!"

"You saved Maryland!"

"Its true! It's *true!*"

Margaret arose and thanked the Assemblymen. She turned to Governor Greene.

"Your confidence in me is deeply appreciated. I shall never forget this day."

Giles came to her, and together they walked through the crowd to the door, and outside to where her horse waited. Giles untied the horse and helped her mount.

He asked: "Shall I ride home with you, Margaret?"

"Oh, no. I'm all right now. Mary's waiting to hear the news, Giles. How she'll enjoy it!"

He waved good-bye and she was off.

In the *Freehold* living room a short time later, Mary listened in amazement to her sister's story.

"It's wonderful, Margaret. Wonderful. And when Cecilius, Lord Baltimore receives Governor Greene's reply, with all those signatures, he'll write you an apology. You'll see."

"He should have written to me in the first place, Mary. I'm his attorney."

It was true. Mary explained that she was not defending My Lord Baltimore. She said: "I'm just assuring you that everything will be all right."

"No, Mary . . . It will not be all right. I am retiring from public life."

Mary stared at her sister, unbelieving.

"We'll move across the border into Virginia, Mary. Giles will of course remain here. He can collect our rents."

"Margaret! You *can't* mean it! Why, Virginia is new and strange and different. All gaiety and dancing! And Maryland's our home."

Margaret, looking at her sister, could not resist a smile. A short time ago, Mary had viewed Maryland with apprehension. Now Virginia had to be approached with fear and reluctance because it was unknown.

She said: "We shall wait until Thomas White returns from England, and ask his opinion as to our making the change. I think he'll agree that we should go."

"Perhaps he'll advise us to stay here," Mary said hopefully.

Thomas White's return was delayed by Civil War in England. He described in a letter to Margaret the beheading of

King Charles I on January 30, 1649. He later wrote of Cromwell's rise to power. Then, at last, he sent word that he'd managed to book passage on a ship.

"In seven days," he wrote, "I sail for Maryland. How I long to see you, Margaret!"

His arrival at the *Freehold* occasioned great rejoicing. When he'd talked at length of England, Margaret mentioned Maryland's Toleration Act, recently passed by the Legislature.

She said: "The Toleration Act provides that no one professing Christianity shall in any way be molested or discountenanced for in respect to his or her religion, nor in the exercise thereof."

"Splendid!" cried Thomas White. "That is sure to have Cromwell's approval."

"A great step forward," Mary said.

Later that evening, when she and Thomas were alone, Margaret laid before him her own personal problem, and also told him of her desire to retire to private life, and move to Virginia.

He agreed that Cecilius, Lord Baltimore, should have first consulted her, as his Maryland attorney, in regard to his disapproval of her sale of his cattle. Lord Baltimore's protest to the Governor, ignoring Margaret, especially in view of all she had done to save the Colony, was inexcusable.

"You see, Thomas, there was not time for me to write for Cecilius, Lord Baltimore's approval or permission, regarding the sale of his cattle. Time was of the essence. If I'd waited for his consent, the settlers might have decided upon drastic action."

"Yes," said Thomas White. "Promptness was absolutely vital."

"And now I should like to move to Virginia, Thomas."

He nodded. "Such a move would give you peace of mind. Virginia's accessible enough, Margaret. I'll be able to visit you often."

"Thomas, I wanted your approval."

He smiled. "You must have known you had it, without asking."

And so, in 1650, Margaret and Mary Brent moved to Virginia and built there a new home and named it *Peace*. From that time on, history has allowed us only one brief glimpse into Margaret's life.

Members of Maryland's Assembly were surprised in 1658 when she suddenly appeared before them as sole heir to a Maryland gentleman's estate. His name was Thomas White.

The Assemblymen, some of them sons or nephews of those who had known her, looked in open curiosity at this famous former citizen who'd helped shape Maryland's beginning history. They noticed that her short red hair had now turned gray; but in her energetic way of speaking, in the eager serious glance of her fine eyes, the years had made no change.

She gave her name, admitted to the age of forty-eight, and stood in thoughtful silence while the will of the deceased was read. Thomas White, the will said, had left her all his possessions as proof of "his love and affection and of his constant wish to marry her."

The younger members stared at her intently now, new admiration in their hearts. She'd craved dangerous living, achieved power, held in her hand Maryland's destiny. And she'd known love. So this—so *this* was Margaret Brent!

2

ANNE HUTCHINSON
A Puritan Love Story
(1591-1653)

Standing straight and dignified in the witness box, as she'd done during the two days of her trial, Anne Hutchinson was thankful she'd worn the gray wool dress that covered her warmly from white Puritan collar to stout shoes. In the unheated, drafty Newtowne courtroom the temperature was close to zero. Every minister and magistrate seated before her on that November day in 1631 could see quite plainly that Anne, early in the new year, would become mother of her sixteenth child.

In spite of their hostile attitude, the Puritan fathers must have admitted that Anne's youthful oval face, rolled-up brown hair, direct gaze of fearless hazel eyes, belied her forty-six years. A modern reporter, covering her trial, would have written: "She's brilliant, beautiful, and has a fine command of English." A twentieth century psychiatrist, noting Anne's erect confidence, tender curve of lips, eyes lighting now and then with some secret happiness, would add: "She is in love."

Anne's glance, directed toward the council table, rested a moment upon Governor John Winthrop in black velvet suit

with white ruffled collar. She looked briefly across faces of
magistrates and ministers, then sought the deep dark eyes of
the Reverend John Cotton. She and John Cotton knew the
seriousness of this moment. If convicted today she faced
banishment from the Colony for life. Such a sentence carried
out during the deep cold of a Massachusetts winter, might
well involve the loss of life itself.

The Reverend John Wilson, Pastor of Morals of the Boston
Church, arose.

He cried: "This woman's theories have become the subject of heated debate in every Boston home!"

"Theories?" asked Anne, looking at him. "I hold no personal theories of religion. Just a belief. I believe that *with love
in your heart you cannot sin.*"

Her words caused the ministers to straighten alertly. One or
two tossed back their capes. The magistrates flushed.

Governor Winthrop sprang up. "By that statement, Mistress Hutchinson, you reject the literal law of the Old Testament and put yourself above and adverse to the Mosaic code.
That's *Antinomianism!*"

"It's heresy!" cried Pastor Wilson.

This word shocked the audience to silence. White-faced
Governor Winthrop sat down; and through the hushed courtroom could be distinctly heard, outside, the falling snow.
Everyone, including Anne herself, was aware that the punishment for heresy was death.

As Pastor Wilson took his seat, the room remained still. No
one seemed to breathe. Anne met John Cotton's glance again.
Would he defend her? She felt her heart swell.

Bible firmly in hand against his ministerial coat, John Cotton walked toward the witness box. His wavy brown hair, cut
long, almost touched the collar of his cape.

Standing between Anne and her accusers, he slowly opened

his Bible. He announced he would read from the Old Testament, Ezekiel 36, 27. His warm, melodious voice quoted: " 'And I will put my Spirit within you and cause you to walk in my statues and ye shall keep my judgments and do them.' "

Anne gave a deep sigh, of relief. As "teacher" in the Boston Church he knew his Scripture. That verse alone would save her.

But Deputy-Governor Dudley sprang to his feet. "John Cotton, have you heard Mistress Hutchinson declare that you alone do preach a Covenant of Grace, while in her opinion all other Boston ministers are unable?"

Anne watched John Cotton's face grow incredibly white. Of the two charges against her, one was traduction; *criticism of the Boston clergy*. Her glance sought John Cotton's. Twenty years of probing his eyes' dark depths had taught her to read them, for between her and the minister, glances had been words. Would he sacrifice his position in the church, risk exile, to save her? Is man's love for woman stronger than ambition in an ambitious man? She knew he weighed his future now, against the weightless force of love!

A magistrate repeated Dudley's question. "Hath Mistress Hutchinson declared all Boston ministers unable except you? The Court demands you answer."

"I do not remember it," said John Cotton.

Anne swayed a moment and had to catch at the witness box's railing for support. No one offered her a chair, nor would she ask for one.

Dudley asked: "What say you, then, John Cotton, of her supposed immediate revelations from God? She hath spoken of God's telling her to leave old England and come to Massachusetts. Is not this blasphemy?"

John Cotton, closing his Bible, said: "There are revelations that come from a study of Scripture . . ."

Dudley broke in: "Sir, you weary me!"

The crowd began to murmur. Anne caught the words: "Doth John Cotton witness for or against Mistress Hutchinson?"

She watched John Cotton glance intently at the ministers, then the magistrates, then at the Governor. These men, of course, held over him the power of life and death. Oh, John, John, her heart cried. It's not easy for you . . .

And as she watched, her thoughts went back swiftly to the steps that had brought her, one by one, from a well-ordered, serene English home to a witness box in this New England courtroom.

So short it all seemed now, in retrospect; Anne's past might have been a day instead of years. She saw the little girl—herself—in the small town of Alford, England, which lay six miles from the North Sea. At the age of thirteen she was seated with her clergyman father, Francis Marbury, at the dining table; with her beautiful mother, Bridget Dryden Marbury; with her many brothers and sisters.

The Marbury children knew that their father had served three prison terms for saying that the High Church Commission's ministers were "unable." On condition that he close his lips to criticism of his "superiors" among the clergy, he'd been allowed to preach here in Alford. He'd kept silent in public. But here at table, in the heart of his family, he spoke his mind.

"My dear," he told his wife, "I know preachers who daily slay souls with cudgels of ignorance and stupidity. I can give you their names."

The expressive face of his wife, who had heard this many times, would offer rapt attention. "Yes, dear, I know that you know."

There would follow a long tirade. Injustice, ignorance, fired

Francis Marbury with holy indignation. The children listened, spellbound.

Now and then, when he felt in the mood, he'd entertain the family with tall tales of Francis Drake, who'd fought the Spanish Armada for weeks in the English Channel. All this happened three years before Anne's birth, but the battle had scattered trophies from wrecked Spanish ships into a thousand British homes, and even now, in the center of the Marbury dining table, a golden plate from which a Spanish pirate used to eat, meekly held English apples and pears.

During dinner one evening, Francis Marbury suddenly asked:

"Anne, how would you like to live in London town?"

"London?" Anne's eyes widened. "Why, father, I'd love it. London's the most wonderful town in all the world."

"At thirteen, Anne, you've not as yet seen all the world," her mother reminded her, smiling.

But Anne's father agreed that London, with its immense population, close to 150,000 people it had in 1604, was indeed the world's finest town. He'd applied for a London appointment.

A year later, when Anne was fourteen, the appointment came. She felt a few moments of regret at leaving Alford where she'd gone to school, and where she knew a nineteen-year-old-boy named William Hutchinson. Still, London was fabulous. She could not wait to see it.

At last the Marbury family was ready for the London journey, and as Anne's father helped her mount the horse she would ride to her new home, she smiled down at friends gathered to say good-bye. The face of William Hutchinson was touched with sadness.

"I'm sure my father will send me to London on business someday," he told Anne.

She nodded, and glanced across Alford's thatched roofs. She was eager to be off. But once more she looked down into William's rather homely face and kind eyes. In his hands he held, respectfully, his broad-brimmed hat.

"Do come if you can," she told him.

She flicked her horse with the reins and galloped off, not knowing it was useless to gallop away from Fate, or William Hutchinson . . .

The next seven years Anne spent in London. In a day when young ladies wore long dresses and high ruffs, and were forbidden to walk alone beyond walled gardens, Anne strolled unattended through London's crowded streets. Westminster Abbey was already 600 years old. Her glance gave it due respect. She stared at the Tower of London, and imagined the men imprisoned there. She stood on London Bridge for a wide, sweeping view of the Thames and longed to explore that river in a little boat.

Suddenly, almost without warning, Francis Marbury died, and for months afterward Anne found it hard to believe she would never hear her dear father's melodious voice again. Often it seemed he was speaking to her. "Things have changed since the death of our good Queen Bess," he'd say. "King James 1 has fined, jailed, cruelly beaten many of our Puritan friends for not attending the Established Church."

All this, of course, was true.

Her father had always liked William Hutchinson who, during the past seven years, had frequently visited the Marbury's in London; and now William and Anne were soon to be married. As Anne strolled, alone, along the bank of the Thames, hearing dip of oars as Mediterranean cargo ships glided by with treasures of velvet and silk, she tried to imagine what life would be like for her as William Hutchinson's wife in the small town of Alford. Alford hadn't changed much since she was a child. She well remembered every house and shop and church.

A few nights before their wedding, Anne and William sat on a bench beneath a spreading tree in the garden of her London house. The darkness, fragrant with summer roses, held small sleepy chirping sounds of birds among breeze-laden leaves.

He caught her hand.

"Anne darling. I'll do my best to give you . . . everything you want."

Everything she wanted? A wave of wonderment swept her heart. *Just what did she want?* Home and children? A safe, domestic, unexciting road? Or more?

"Anne, I'll make one promise. *Nothing will matter to me but your happiness.*"

A gust of summer wind swept by with silent laughter. It caught his words and hoarded them. They'd be scattered, winged seeds, upon the years to come.

Anne and William were married in London on August 9, 1612. She was twenty-one and he twenty-six. They moved into a large house in Alford, where William worked in his father's shop. The senior Hutchinson, a silk merchant, was very prosperous.

Anne found herself mistress of a home, with servants and a garden, with friendly neighbors and a nearby church. She read the Bible daily, as her father had taught her to do, and tried to discuss various texts with William across the dining table. But his cultural background, where the Scriptures were concerned, did not match her own; and there were times when she craved to explore the deeper meanings of the new King James' version of the Bible with someone who possessed her late father's intellectual curiosity.

William, who'd inherited his ancestors' business skill and

shrewdness, now found life rich and satisfying. He arose early to open his father's shop, and asked no further blessings than the fun of improving each financial daily hour until, toward evening, he could hurry home to Anne.

They attended church on Sundays and this pleasant pattern; work, relaxation in the evenings, Sunday worship, continued until their first child Edward, was born a year after their marriage. And then, on a Spring Sabbath morning, Anne came to her husband with a request that was to change the entire course of their lives. The request, when granted, would serve to place her name on pages of histories read by countless generations to come.

She said: "The town of Boston has a new young minister whose voice is said to be remarkable, his sermons profound. He preaches at St. Botolph's Church. Shall we ride there this morning?"

He smiled down at her, thinking how beautiful she looked to him today, and always. Good thing their baby, Edward, resembled his mother, not his father. He bent to kiss Anne. "Darling, you can't be serious. A twenty-four mile horseback ride, *just to hear a sermon?*"

"I'd like to go, William. He's a Trinity College man and takes a firm Puritan stand. His name's John Cotton."

As he continued to look at her, William realized that sermons, to the daughter of a clergyman, were almost as important as was business to him. He remembered, too, a certain promise given in a London garden. He walked out to the stable and ordered two horses saddled.

A few hours later, seated beside Anne in John Cotton's crowded church, William watched his wife's ardent listening and felt repaid for the sacrifice of his Sabbath comfort. She seemed lost in the spell of the minister's words.

It was true, William admitted to himself, that young John Cotton's voice held a soothing cadence. Put a fellow to sleep. John Cotton, at twenty-eight, six years older than Anne, had wavy brown hair, deep dark brown eyes, and a smile that warmed your heart. William could not help noticing the minister's expressive gestures, his thin, fine hands.

The Reverend John Cotton was saying: "All that one needs is His spirit—*which is love*—in one's heart."

Anne felt the words in every cell of her body. Yes, yes, yes! That is it, everything: love in one's heart!

The twenty-four mile horseback ride home was as nothing to her. Anne all but forgot her husband at her side. She relived the hearing of John Cotton's voice, saw again his smile as she'd told him, after the sermon, how much his words had meant to her.

The memory of Sunday remained with Anne all week, helped her rise gladly before daybreak to read her Bible, made light of her work: overseeing the curing of meat, weaving of wool, baking of great loaves of bread. In the afternoons, rocking young Edward to sleep, she thought: "All that one needs is . . . *love in one's heart.*"

Next Sunday, at breakfast, she asked William to take her again to Boston.

"Have we no able preachers here in Alford?" he asked.

She smiled at him, remembering that her father had served prison terms for calling certain preachers "unable."

"John Cotton's sermon is more than able," she told him.

"A sermon's only a sermon," he argued. "To me, one sounds very like another."

But it was characteristic of William Hutchinson that presently he got up from the table and went out to have two horses saddled. He rode with Anne to hear John Cotton. He

rode with her the same twenty-four miles each Sabbath for
the next twenty years.

During these twenty years thirteen more children were
born to Anne and William. Susannah was born in 1614, but
later died. Richard was born in 1615, Faith in 1617, Bridget,
1618, Francis in 1622. In 1623, Elizabeth and William were
born, but both died young. There was Samuel in 1624, Anne
in 1625, Mary in 1627, Katherine in 1629. A boy, born in
1631, was again given the name of William; and a girl, born
in 1633, was again called Susannah.

It was now 1633, and Edward had reached the age of
twenty. Two years before, on the death of his father, William Hutchinson as eldest son had inherited a considerable
estate.

At the age of forty, Anne was still beautiful, with sweet
contour of face, erect and graceful carriage, an inner aliveness untouched by the years. Time, however, had added
weight to William's figure, thickened his nose, accented his
homeliness. It had in no way changed his heart, which ever
lifted to the wonder of Anne.

John Cotton, because of his departure from usages prescribed by the Established Church, was being threatened with
prison. He had refused to wear a surplice while preaching,
had not required his congregation to kneel in prayer, had
ordered the stained glass windows of his church removed.
For the past thirteen years, ever since the Separatists had in
1620 sailed in their three-masted ship, *the Mayflower*, to freedom of worship in the New World, John Cotton had been
advocating, to St. Botolph's congregation, freedom from rites
and ritual.

One afternoon William Hutchinson came home from his

shop with news for Anne: "Tonight John Cotton is to be arrested."

"But it's unthinkable!" Anne cried. "He mustn't be thrown into prison. Can't you do something to help?"

He looked at her in sympathy. After a thoughtful moment, he said: "If he could be induced to wear a disguise, I think I might help him to escape."

She caught William's hand. In gratitude. She knew now that John Cotton would be safe.

And so it happened that, late that night, William Hutchinson journeyed to London with a man servant. The "servant," successful in eluding police, found sanctuary in London and later wrote to Anne and William, offering to take Edward, their son, with him to Boston, Massachusetts. Edward could sail with John Cotton on the next vessel leaving the Kentish Coast. There were many fine opportunities for young men in the New World.

On a dark night, shortly after this, Anne and William watched Edward mount his horse and gallop off to meet John Cotton at the Downs on the Kentish coast. They would sail on the *Griffin*, and with favorable winds Edward and John Cotton would arrive in Boston, Massachusetts, sixty days later. When sounds of Edward's horse's hoofs could be heard only in the distant darkness and indistinctly, William put an endearing arm about his wife.

"Anne, of all our children, Edward looks most like you."

She could not speak. She had heard the same words from John Cotton over the years. "When I look into young Edward's eyes," he'd told her, "I see his mother."

Life in Alford now became for Anne an endless series of

dull tasks. Each morning the older children left for school and did not return until late afternoon. She busied herself with the younger girls and boys; she inspected the servants' work, she found tasks of darning and sewing, or planning of next day's activities. She drove herself relentlessly, as if fearing to sit and dream.

One day, while reading the Bible, she heard the Lord's voice.

The Lord said: "Be not afraid or discouraged; *but go to the New World.*"

Suddenly, in all England, no spot was as lonely, barren, desolate as Alford. That evening she said to William:

"I long with all my heart to go to Massachusetts."

He looked at her, shocked at the drastic step this would involve. Not only would they have to uproot their large family, but he'd be forced to sell his prosperous business and begin again at the age of forty-eight in an unknown land.

It was true, of course, that Charles I had just dissolved the Parliament, and this made for unsettled conditions in England.

"The *Griffin* sails again for Boston in a few months," Anne said gently. "Can we be ready?"

It was as simple as that.

To pay for passage for his ten children, also for Anne, himself and their three servants, William sold his Alford shop. There should be room for a new shop in Boston, where he could sell linen, wool and other merchandise to the town's one thousand settlers.

He began to study the history of Boston. King Charles I, in 1628, had granted a large tract of land in New England to the Massachusetts Bay Company in return for a supply of fish and furs. The exact boundary of this tract had not been fixed; but now, six years later, the town of Boston, with an area of four square miles, was the tract's principal trading center.

The Hutchinsons sailed for Boston on the *Griffin* in July, 1634. When they landed in Massachusetts, they'd be met by Edward, who had been in Boston for a year.

The voyage required seventy days and Anne, now feeling that a giant who'd been riding on her shoulders had lifted himself off, converted shipboard life into a continuous party. When meals were to be cooked, she took her place with the other women at the open hearth, joked about the mouldy bread, made fun of the salt meat and peas porridge, until the entire lantern-lit hold echoed with their laughter. During long afternoons on deck she entertained the other passengers, men and women, with her father's tales of the long-ago Spanish Armada and Sir Francis Drake.

Now and then conversation became serious, touching on churches and creeds.

"True religion is a very simple thing," Anne said. "I can put it into fifteen words: *all that we need is the Spirit of God —which is love—in our hearts.*"

"What about sinners?" demanded a man sternly.

She looked at him. "With love in one's heart, it is impossible to sin."

The men and women stared at her. Her pure logic had dragged them beyond their depth, leaving them speechless.

As the ship neared Boston, Anne felt excitement in every vein. She did not want to share these last moments with husband or children, but found a place at the rail and stared out at the shimmering waves, cloudless sky, bright sunshine. No wonder poets likened sunlight to love. It infused one's body with the same illuminating warmth. Sunlight was part of God, of course. And God was love.

Now, at the journey's end, all its hardships had turned into a dream. All her past life had turned into a dream. Only here before her, in Boston, lay reality.

As the Hutchinsons walked down the gangplank to Boston's wharf, Edward rushed forward to take his mother in his arms. Even as she embraced him, Anne saw John Cotton standing nearby.

The Reverend John Cotton came and took her hands in both his own, and she felt his palms against hers tremble. She noted his Puritan cape, the skull cap on his longish brown hair. His dark eyes told her what could not be said in words.

William Hutchinson came toward them.

"We've sailed three thousand miles through three thousand dangers," he said to John Cotton.

The minister grasped his hand. "Welcome to Boston!"

All the Hutchinsons and John Cotton walked along the wharf and toward the large house in which they were to stay until their own home was built. Anne's heart sang. What mattered that Boston's narrow crooked streets presented a collection of huts? Nothing mattered, for in all the world there was no better place than Boston. Hadn't God told her to come?

The Hutchinsons' first few months in four-year-old Boston saw Anne adjusting easily to Colonial life. Once their new frame house, in the heart of town, was completed (at what is now the corner of Washington and School Streets) she began to take an active part in the community's affairs. She and William were admitted to membership in the Boston Church where John Wilson served as pastor and John Cotton was "teacher."

It surprised her to discover that few Boston women were able to discuss political matters. They stared at her in blank astonishment whenever she led conversation outside the home's safe walls. Their lack of broader interest was not due to stupidity, she decided; nor could the town's lack of a library, or daily newspapers or daily mail account for it. Anne told herself it was caused by the suffocating load of household labor pressed upon the wives by austere Puritan fathers. She must do what she could to lighten this burden.

The success of her efforts to open the minds of Puritan women surprised even Anne herself. Whenever she attended a "spinning circle" or christening, or any social function, women bombarded her with questions that betrayed their awakened mental awareness. Even the Governor's wife, Mrs. John Winthrop, made an entry in her diary: "Until Anne Hutchinson came to Boston, the women of our town had no opinions of their own."

Anne kept her husband and children happy. The three servants that William Hutchinson had brought from England were much treasured here in this practically servantless Colony, and Anne managed to teach all three the art of baking bread in iron basins among hot hearth ashes, and salting pork in great tubs.

When the younger children returned from Dame School in the afternoons, she listened to their talk of naughty boys being spanked with an oaken ruler, or wearing dunce caps because they couldn't add or spell. She'd try in the evenings to erase the day's austerity with checkboard tournaments, and would present the winners with crunchy quince tarts of her own baking, while she gave the losers thick slices of fresh bread and honey.

She went on Sundays to the Boston Church, whose sawdust floor and backless wooden benches and oil-paper-glass in the windows drew from Anne no complaint. John Cotton's buoyant sermons fell across her heart like warm sunlight; and she longed to pass on their vital truths to her Puritan women friends.

During the mornings she often walked along Boston's narrow streets, and her quick sympathy went out to Indian squaws who trudged from door to door trying to sell the hand-made birch brooms they carried in neat bundles on their backs. Anne felt compassion for an elderly man wearing about his neck the cruel, heavy wooden yoke bearing the letter "D" for drunkenness. She looked with interest and a touch of sadness at the pale young apprentice boy whose round, flat pie-dish hat sat strangely upon his shaven head.

Her walks sometimes took her to homes of the sick, for she was skilled at nursing. It was rumored that her presence hastened the patient's recovery.

One day during a walk, Anne decided upon a method of spreading John Cotton's teaching among the Puritan women. She would listen carefully to his Sunday sermons, then invite the women to her home on Monday afternoons for repetition of his sermons and a discussion of John Cotton's philosophy. A fine idea!

During the weeks that followed, the Monday afternoon gatherings at Anne's house became the talk of Boston. So many Puritan wives crowded into her living room they were forced to pour into the hall, even out upon the lawn, listening through open windows.

Anne drove home certain basic truths:

"Menial work alone does not make of one a Christian."

"Wearing of plain and ugly clothing has nothing whatever to do with true Christianity."

"True Christianity is a simple thing. It's nothing more or less than the Spirit of God—which is love—in your heart."

Boston women accepted all this with an ardor that alarmed

their husbands. And when the meetings had been going on for several weeks, the husbands held a meeting of their own and finally voted to send several of their members to interview William Hutchinson.

At his shop, William received them kindly, offered chairs, discussed the weather, the price of wool. But when they suggested that he forbid his wife's Monday afternoon meetings, his face flushed with anger.

"My wife and I do not give each other orders," he said. "And all her good works have my complete sanction. In truth, I am more nearly tied to her than to the church itself."

The interview was over. The Puritan fathers, reluctantly arose and departed.

But now Anne's Monday afternoon meetings were discussed in every home. The town's leaders remained bitterly opposed to them, and to her views; but one or two ministers dared to say openly that they agreed with her in that "when one's heart is right, one cannot sin."

Fourteen months after Anne's arrival in Massachusetts a ship, the *Abigail*, brought to Boston a handsome, twenty-three year old Englishman; Sir Harry Vane. His father was Privy Councilor to King Charles I, and the young man became John Cotton's house guest. In due time he met Anne Hutchinson and gave her his whole-hearted admiration, and her religious theories his ardent support.

The coming of Harry Vane widened Anne's interests, and she began now to look into the political affairs of the Colony under Vane's guidance, for he was skilled in law. Within two months he had assumed leadership among Boston's elders, and after meeting with the city fathers during the day he would see Anne in her home that evening and discuss various problems of state with her.

Ships were arriving now more frequently from England,

and Anne received letters from her Alford relatives and friends. Some of the friends frequently took flowers for the graves of Anne's three young children buried in Alford, and this thoughtfulness touched her deeply.

She learned from an aunt that her young cousin, John Dryden, born in 1631 and now four years old, could actually say the entire alphabet correctly. She was proud of him. She had no way of knowing that John Dryden would grow up to write some of England's finest poetry.

In March of 1636 Anne's fifteenth child was born, and she and William named him Zuriel. One can imagine eighty or more Puritan wives, attending Anne's Monday meetings, pausing at Zuriel's crib to lavish "oh's" and "ah's."

The Monday meetings went on for three years and during this time the Puritan fathers gradually developed toward them and toward Anne, an almost pathological hatred. But they had not yet decided upon action.

When Harry Vane became Governor of Massachusetts, Anne had a staunch defender in high office. Her brother-in-law, John Wheelwright, with his wife, Mary, who was William Hutchinson's sister, had just arrived from England. Wheelwright, a Cambridge man, had been a classmate of Oliver Cromwell.

Anne emphasized, at her meetings with the Puritan women, that in her opinion John Cotton was the only Boston minister who preached that "the person of the Holy Spirit dwells in a justified person." After John Wheelwright's arrival, she told the women that Boston now had two ministers who were "sealed with the covenant of Grace."

The other ministers bitterly resented this. They invited Anne to meet before them late one summer evening of 1637, in John Cotton's house. "Explain your Boston two ministers statement," they demanded.

Anne defended herself brilliantly. Finally she said: "If I must withhold from any of you my inner Christian thoughts, then religious freedom has not followed us into the New World."

But a few Sundays later John Wheelwright preached such a disturbing sermon that he was charged with sedition by Boston's ministers and magistrates. Governor Vane made an effort to defend him, but this defense lost Vane his Governorship. John Winthrop was later elected Governor in Vane's place.

Wheelwright, banished from the Colony, went to what is now New Hampshire, and was joined there by his wife and children. He became pastor of a church.

It is interesting to note that handsome Harry Vane, who returned to England, served under King Charles I until 1649, when that monarch was beheaded. He then served under the Cromwells, father and son. But when the House of Stuart was restored to England's throne under Charles II, Harry Vane, now fifty years old, was arrested for "opposing liberalism," confined in the Tower, then beheaded.

Back in Boston, Massachusetts, Anne Hutchinson was accused of a crime in August, 1637. The crime: *Antinomianism*. The word means "against the law." Antinomians, a sect, flourished in Central Europe a hundred years before. Antinomians believed that goodness was a matter of the heart; they also believed in the supremacy of Spirit over law.

On August 30, 1637, Massachusetts ministers and magistrates held a Synod, an Ecclesiastical Council, in the village of Newtowne which is now Cambridge. The Synod met near the spot where today stands Harvard College, and its meetings lasted for twenty-four days.

Synod members decided that women's meetings such as those held at Anne Hutchinson's home were "disorderly."

The members drew up certain rules regarding "the Spirit of Christ in a believer's heart" and then laid the groundwork for civil action against Anne.

In November Anne was directed to appear before a General Court presided over by Governor Winthrop and Deputy Governor Thomas Dudley. William Hutchinson, apprehensive of the trial's outcome, left Boston and journeyed to the new settlement established on Rhode Island by Roger Williams. He took all the Hutchinson children with him, and the older ones cared for the younger. Anne knew she must now face trial alone; but she knew, too, that whatever the verdict her family would be safe and free.

In the witness box now she was brought back sharply to the present by Pastor Wilson's voice.

"What say you, Mr. Cotton, to her preaching to the wives of Boston?"

"I did not preach," Anne broke in. "I discussed Mr. Cotton's sermons."

"Who told you to do this?" Pastor Wilson demanded.

"God. He made me know I had to do it. When I feel His Spirit within me, I must do what I think is right."

Sudden murmurings through the courtroom told her she had again awakened Puritan taboo against special revelation. She felt hate-hardened eyes. She looked at John Cotton. Would he explain to them? Would he put into ministerial language the great, enlightning truth he had written upon her young heart—how many years ago—in Alford?

She said: "My teacher knows my judgment. I have never kept my judgment from him. He will tell you what I mean."

John Cotton's startled glance came to hers and an expression in his eyes filled Anne with shocked benumbment.

Pastor Wilson turned to him. "If as she says you know her judgment, what say you, Mr. Cotton?"

John Cotton said: *"I think that God hath let her fall into a manifest lie."*

The blow of his words took a moment to reach Anne's heart. It could not be he who had spoken. But even as she denied his words, they burned within her like spreading molten lead. She could only cry, silently: *"Forgive him, Father. Forgive him . . .*

She stood motionless, staring at the floor, taking no further part in the courtroom discussion.

Vaguely, she was aware of John Cotton's voice saying that morals were not a Teacher's but a Pastor's province. Thus was her "crime" being shifted into Pastor Wilson's realm.

Suddenly the room grew deathly quiet. Anne glanced at Governor Winthrop, who was rising from his chair.

The Governor said: "I hereby declare you, Mrs. Hutchinson, to be banished from our jurisdiction."

Anne's eyes met his stern ones. "Wherefor am I banished? I desire to know."

"The Court knows wherefor, and is satisfied."

The Governor advanced to the witness box, helped Anne down, and walked beside her to the courtroom door. Not once did she glance toward John Cotton.

During the next few days, after her sentence, Anne found herself in custody of Joseph Weld, in his home, in the town of Roxbury. The reason given for this delay in allowing her to join her husband was the wintry Massachusetts weather; but the Boston ministers' true motive for detaining her was their hope she might be urged to admit error in her thinking. She was visited day after day by those who tried to force her to recant, yet she stood firm. She was finally lodged in the home of John Cotton and under persistent mental pressure was said to have acknowledged she might be partly in the wrong. But when taken to church soon after this, and questioned before the congregation, there was no recanting on Anne's part. She spoke out freely, as always. She had not changed.

Pastor Wilson cried: "Then, in the name of Jesus Christ, and of this church, I command you, as a Leper, to withdraw yourself out of this congregation."

Anne withdrew.

She paused at the door to say: "The Lord judgeth not as man judgeth. Better to be cast out of the church than to deny Christ."

She turned and walked out. And as she went down the steps she grew conscious of a sense of freedom and relief. It was over. Now she could start her six-day journey across the sixty chill, snowy miles to join her husband and children in the home he'd made for her in the town of Pocasset (later named Portsmouth) on Rhode Island.

Anne arrived at Pocasset completely exhausted. Soon afterward she gave birth to her sixteenth child. The baby was born dead.

In a few weeks, however, she was taking an active part in the new settlement, and become a leader in the Pocasset church. In the evenings, seated with her family in the spacious living room of her home, around the cheerful, blazing hearth, Boston seemed far away and almost long ago. Here, in Roger Williams' settlement, she had found peace.

When the Hutchinsons had lived in Pocasset about three years, Anne was surprised to receive a visit one afternoon from several elders of the Boston church. She invited them into the living room and offered them chairs.

The visitors, in their Puritan garb, explained that repentance might re-admit her to the Boston Church.

She arose from her chair and stood rigidly before them.

"Repentance? For what?"

They tried to tell her.

When they had finished speaking, she said: "I shall not return. Nor do I acknowledge the Boston Church to be a Church of Christ."

The elders finally departed. They went out of Anne's house and down the narrow street to William Hutchinson's shop. William was standing behind the counter.

"Thy good business sense is needed in the Massachusetts Colony, William Hutchinson," they said. "Why exile yourself in Rhode Island just because your wife . . ."

William leaned toward them, not knowing that his large face had flushed. He said:

"My wife is a dear saint and servant of God!"

The Puritan elders departed.

That evening, after her family had gone to bed, Anne sat alone before the hearth fire in her living room and thought of John Cotton. Had today's visit from the elders been his idea? She would never know.

Memory, for a moment, began to light the days of her youth, before she'd become aware of John Cotton's existence. Suppose she had never met him. Suppose William had refused to take her to hear him preach that Sunday morning. Would she have gone alone? No. And this meant she'd not have come to Massachusetts.

Suppose she could actually live life over. Would she, if she had the power to change her course, omit her meeting with John Cotton? Oh, no. No! She would not trade. Not for a thousand peaceful years in Alford. Better—*even as it turned out*—to have known love . . .

In 1642 William Hutchinson suddenly died. Without William's protection, Anne felt the need of placing greater distance between her family and the Boston Puritan fathers, who were now claiming Rhode Island as part of the Massachusetts Bay Colony grant.

Several of Anne's older children had married and settled in their own homes, but with the younger boys and girls she set out for what is now the southeastern section of New York State. The site she selected on which to build their new home was in the township of Eastchester, on Shore Road.

The smooth pavement of today's Shore Road holds gleaming cars that glide past beautiful estates. And it is difficult to see it through Anne's eyes, for then the road skirted virgin acres not far from a Siwanoy Indian Village.

She paid a Mr. James Sands to build a house for her. But while he and his helper were at work they were interrupted by Indians who advised him in sign language to leave. This happened twice. Sands returned much of the money to Anne, who was forced to hire another builder to complete her house and barn.

Once settled in the new home with her family, however, Anne tried to make friends with the Indians, who dropped by now and then to look around. She hired white men to plow the fields. She listened to neighbors' stories of savages who, resenting the white man's intrusion hereabout, raided the surrounding settlements.

On an August evening in 1653 a band of Indians encircled Anne's new home. They set fire to the house. As Anne and her children ran out, they were murdered, with one excep-

tion. The Indians spared the life of little eight-year-old Su-
sanna Hutchinson, and carried her away.

There is no record of this tragic scene, but its frightful
details may well be imagined. No doubt Anne fought des-
perately for her life and the lives of her children. No doubt
her stout resistance, to the last, won Indian respect.

So died one of America's bravest.

If she could return to today's America, Anne would be
surprised to see her marble statue on Boston's State House
lawn. It would interest her to learn that her great-great
grandson, Thomas Hutchinson, last Royal Governor of Massachusetts, refused clearance of the tea ship papers in 1773,
and thus set the table for the Boston Tea Party.

But her greatest satisfaction would come from reading a
certain sentence in the Constitution of the United States.
It says: "Congress shall make no law abridging the freedom
of speech." Anne Hutchinson helped write those words. For
them she gave her life.

3

ELIZA LUCAS PINCKNEY
(1723-1793)

As she stood upon Charles Town's wharf that June morning of 1739 to say good-bye to her father, sixteen year old Eliza Lucas tried not to let the watching sailors see her tears. Soon Major Lucas, her handsome father in his blue British uniform, would walk up the gangplank of the man of war and be off to Antigua in the West Indies.

"All aboard!" boomed a harsh voice.

Eliza felt the sound in her heart. Her father bent down and kissed her.

"Terrible to have to leave you here, my darling. But just as soon as I can I'll send for you and Polly and Mama. I promise."

"Papa, I love it here in Carolina. I know I was born in Antigua, but Carolina's *home!* Send for Mama and Polly, but let me stay."

"Stay here all by yourself?"

"All by myself, Papa. *Please!*"

He caught both her hands and looked down intently at her luminous small face, shining fair curls, buoyant aliveness. A fresh breeze, sharp with sea smells, billowed Eliza's long taffeta dress and tried to pull off her wide-brimmed yellow straw hat.

He said: "Now run along home, my darling. I'll watch you to the chaise."

She glanced at the two-masted sailing ship, the man of war, tugging at its moorings, eager to be off.

She said quickly: "I'll take care of Mama. And manage our three plantations. And write you often."

He nodded, and let go of her hands.

She gathered up her long skirt and ran to the waiting chaise whose door was quickly opened by a liveried Negro. Tears blinded her so that she could not see the step, but the man helped her in. When she was seated, he closed the door, sprang to the driver's seat and took the reins. He shouted to the horses. They were off.

She wished Papa had let her wait and watch the ship sail, but of course he wanted her to get back to Mama as soon as possible. He'd be miles away by this time tomorrow. She closed her eyes and leaned against the cushioned back of the chaise whose turning wheels said: *he's gone . . . he's gone . . .*

When she opened her eyes again, the chaise was hurrying along a tree-lined road that led, seventeen miles distant, to the Lucas home. Glancing through the window, she saw passing fields of rice and corn. The Lucas plantations looked better than these, because Papa never thought of a field, even a never-plowed field, as "virgin acres." He tried to make restitution to the soil. Papa realized that long before the white man first saw Carolina in 1520, generations of Indians had farmed this land. Virgin acres indeed!

Suddenly, Eliza grew conscious of enchantment in the air. They were nearing Belmont, the home of Colonel Charles Pinckney, a forty year old lawyer who shared her love for farming, art, music, books. They had only to exchange a few words and up would spring, between them, an animated conversation.

Eliza and the Colonel's invalid wife were close friends; and she was made welcome always at Belmont, where the Pinckneys lived, for several months each year.

She caught a glimpse through the trees of Belmont's landscaped grounds that sloped to the edge of the Cooper River. Eliza knew these grounds well; the house too, with its panelled walls, spacious rooms. Many an evening had she spent with Colonel Pinckney in Belmont's library whose walls of books were lighted by brilliant candles in branching silver candlesticks on polished tables.

She leaned forward in the chaise to ask the coachman to turn into Belmont's driveway. Then she checked the impulse. Wasn't Mama waiting at home, eager to hear all details of Papa's departure? She'd want to know whether the man of war looked sea worthy. She'd ask if Eliza thought it would carry him safely not only through storms, but through possible encounters with Spanish pirates. Eliza, leaning back, waited while the chaise passed Belmont and hurried on toward the Lucas plantation.

Eliza's younger sister, Polly, at boarding school in Charles Town, had not been permitted to come to the wharf to see her father off. Papa hadn't wanted this. Eliza's two brothers, George and Tom, were at school in London. Not long ago, Eliza had been attending school in London, too. And she thought of herself as a loyal subject of King George II.

At last the horses drew up before the Lucas home. The coachman jumped down, opened the door for Eliza, and she got out. She ran up the front steps and a Negro boy opened the front door for her. She thanked him and hurried along the hall to her mother's bedroom.

Mrs. Lucas' frail health confined her to this bedroom unless an unusually attractive social function lured her into an evening gown and out of the house. Now she sat in her cushioned chair wearing a flame-color housegown of silk, and when Eliza came in she leaned eagerly forward for her daughter's kiss.

"Tell me everything, dear. How did Papa look? What did he say? What kept you so long? Perhaps you'd better rest a moment after that tiresome drive."

Eliza tossed her straw hat on the table beside her mother's chair and pulled up a straight chair.

"I'm not tired at all," she said, sitting down. "Papa worried at the thought of leaving you and Polly here. Said he'd send for you—for us—as soon as possible."

Mrs. Lucas sighed. "When *do* you think we'll be able to leave this God forsaken colony, Eliza? Six months? A year?"

"Now, *Mama!*" Eliza said, and quickly changed the subject. She described the scene on the wharf, the man of war, the sailors, sunshine on the lapping waves. Mrs. Lucas listened eagerly. Her eyes were as blue as Eliza's, but lacked their animation. Her body, fashioned as sweetly as her daughter's lacked Eliza's zest for life.

"But, Eliza, when do you think he *will* send for us?"

Eliza flushed. Her tone grew persuasive. "Mama, darling, you love the parties here in Carolina. You and Papa attended one only last week, and you loved it. And don't forget the ball at Belmont next Wednesday evening."

Mrs. Lucas smiled. "Yes. And you'll go with me of course, Eliza. Colonel and Mrs. Pinckney will expect you. You avoid so many social functions I feel embarrassed, making excuses for you."

"If I let them, social functions would swallow all my time, Mama."

"Swallow your time! How absurd that sounds from a girl of sixteen! Like a miser counting his gold."

"Time is worth more than gold, Mama."

"Nonsense. And I'll tell you something, Eliza. What with rising at five in the morning and working all day, you'll be an old woman before you're a young one. You may perhaps spoil your chance of marriage."

Eliza's laughter brightened the room. "Mama, if I look older than sixteen, it's because I *am* older. I sleep less than eight hours, and thus I live longer. That's mathematically true."

The mother sighed. She looked at her daughter without understanding. She said: "Tell me again, Eliza, just what it is you do all day."

Eliza counted off the hours on her fingers. "I rise at five, read till seven, then go out and inspect the Negro cabins. I have breakfast at eight, then practise music for an hour, then study French. Next I try to learn shorthand from a book Colonel Pinckney lent me, but I'm a great dunce at it."

The mother gave her a look. "I should think you would be!"

"Next, Mama, I teach little Negro girls to read. Afterward I ride over our plantations . . ."

Mrs. Lucas held up her hand. "Enough! Makes me tired, just to hear it." She closed her eyes. "I think it's time for my nap."

Eliza got up, kissed her mother gently, took her hat and tip-toed from the room.

The following Wednesday evening Eliza sat with her mother in the stern of a forty-foot cypress canoe that was being paddled down the river by singing Negroes. Their voices kept in rhythm with the paddle strokes. In her dance frock of blue brocade under a cream silk evening cloak, Eliza looked as lovely as a moonbeam. Her mother, in lavender silk, with black velvet wrap, might have been mistaken for Eliza's older sister.

The starlit night air held a scent of jasmine. Mrs. Lucas was remembering another such night, in far-off Antigua, when she'd said "yes" to Eliza's father.

Eliza, enjoying the starlight, the dark river, the Negroes' singing, held a book in tight fingers; *Plutarch's Lives*. She would return it to Colonel Pinckney and tell him about its narrow escape from the flames last night.

She had been reading the book in an easy chair before her bedroom's grate fire when the gray-haired housekeeper, Mrs. Holoday, came in. Mrs. Holoday, the white woman in charge of all Negro house slaves, had since Eliza's early childhood, looked upon herself as a second mother to her.

"It's past midnight, Miss Eliza. And tomorrow night's the Belmont ball. Time you was in bed, isn't it?" She came closer. "What is that you're reading?"

Eliza held up the book.

"Another of those dry, heavy books! I declare, Miss Eliza! Give it to me!"

Before Eliza realized the book's danger, Mrs. Holoday had snatched *Plutarch's Lives* and would have tossed it into the blazing fire, but for Eliza's quick rescue.

"Dear Mrs. Holoday, please don't worry about my reading." Eliza spoke gently, but her heart was racing. "Please go to bed, yourself." She settled back in the chair, found her place in the book. "I've just a little more. I must finish this tonight."

But Mrs. Holoday was like a tigress bent on rescuing her

cub. She went into a high-pitched tirade. Did Eliza mean to read herself mad? Young ladies eager for a good marriage did not fill their heads with such as Plutarch.

"Now, Mrs. Holoday, *please* . . ."

"I suppose you'll talk Plutarch at the ball tomorrow night." Eliza smiled. "Oh, no."

"Oh, yes, you will. And every young man will run for his life."

"Mrs. Holoday, I promise. I'll talk only of moonlight and peach blossoms."

Finally, after much more argument, Mrs. Holoday reluctantly went out and closed the bedroom door.

Now, as the canoe skimmed over the water, Eliza remembered her peach blossom promise. Well, Colonel Pinckney could talk of such, if necessary. Thank goodness it was never necessary between them.

"We're almost there," said Mrs. Lucas.

A few moments later, the Negroes grounded the big canoe and helped Eliza and her mother out. They walked together up the river bank, lighted by torches held high by Belmont Negroes, listening to the music and laughter that floated from the open windows of the brilliantly illuminated house.

At the front door, young men bowed to them, young women in elaborate gowns curtsied and smiled. Servants removed Eliza's and her mother's wraps. Then she and Mrs. Lucas made their way to where Colonel Pinckney stood, with Mrs. Pinckney beside him in her wheel chair.

They exchanged greetings, talked a moment, and then the Colonel took Plutarch from Eliza's hands. She told him, with a smile, about the book's escape from burning. He said: "Meet me in the library after dinner, and I'll give you a new book."

She nodded, and turned to a young man who came up to ask her to dance. Next moment, moving off with her partner to join other couples on the crowded ballroom floor, she remembered her promise to Mrs. Holoday. She spoke only of peach blossoms and related subjects, she laughed gaily, and she danced every dance until dinner was announced.

In the immense dining hall, the guests were seated at a long, damask-covered table set with gleaming silver and priceless china. Dinner was an elaborate affair. The guests were served turkey, duck, venison, turtle, many vegetables, and rice. All was "washed down" with claret, port and Madeira.

After dinner, violin music drew the dancers back to the ballroom. They'd pause now and then in their own dancing to walk out on the broad piazza and look down at the swaying Negroes on the lawn, dancing to the lovely music that floated from the open windows. Flickering torches in tall containers lighted the scene with bright unreality.

As she watched the dancing Negroes, Eliza kept wondering how to get away from her present partner who was telling her pleasant nonsense about her golden hair, her smile, her graceful dancing. She was remembering Colonel Pinckney's suggestion that, after dinner, she meet him in the library.

At last she managed to think of an excuse, and left the young man alone on the piazza. She hurried down the familiar hallway to a familiar room whose door now stood open. She entered the brilliant library—its walls lined with books. And she was studying a row of books on a lower shelf when she knew, without turning, that he had come in.

He came to her and reached for a book upon an upper shelf above her head. He said:

"I hope you've been enjoying the party."

"I have indeed, Colonel Pinckney." She gave him a smile. "All evening I've talked of butterflies and primroses. Nothing —but *nothing*—more important."

He laughed, and then studied her with serious eyes. "You

look a little like a primrose, yourself, tonight. I'm sorry I've
had to give up the pleasure of dancing. Otherwise I would
have asked for one with you."

She nodded. Yes, since his dear wife had been confined to
her wheel chair, he had not danced. Eliza was aware of this.

He gave her the book he had selected, and she glanced at
its title. She raised surprised brows.

"Virgil? You want me involved in storms, battles and tem-
pests, Colonel? To shudder while I read?"

He laughed. "You'll find no shudders here, Eliza. This book
will instruct you in agriculture, and entertain you. Virgil's
writing of Italy, and as we have much the same climate, he
might as well be writing of Carolina."

She smiled and hugged the book close. "Oh, thank you!"

They stood in silence a moment, knowing that they could
not start a conversation with his guests waiting for him in the
outside world. And so they walked out of the library and
found Mrs. Pinckney and chatted with her until guests came
and joined them and the talk became general. Presently others
came up to say good-bye and to tell the Pinckneys they'd
greatly enjoyed the evening. Then Eliza went to look for her
mother. It was time to leave for home.

During the next few weeks, Eliza was kept very busy overseeing her father's three plantations. "Wappoo," on which
she and her mother lived contained 600 acres. "Garden Hill,"
forty miles distant, had 1,500, and "Waccamaw," eighty miles
to the northeast of the Lucas home, was a 3000-acre plantation. A Mr. Murray had charge of Garden Hill, a Mr. Star-
ratt of Waccamaw, and each plantation was completely self-
supporting, growing its food, salting its meats, doing its own
carpenter and blacksmith work. Many boats that sailed down
the Ashely and Cooper rivers with supplies were built upon
these plantations.

On all three plantations were Negro slaves and white indentured servants. The white servants were skilled in spinning, weaving, boot-making. They also made bricks. And when hostile Indians threatened, it was the white servants who picked up guns.

It seemed incredible that a girl of sixteen should be in charge of these three small worlds. But she discharged her responsibilities as well as if she'd been much older. And as well as if she'd been a man.

When she inspected a Negro cabin, she not only insisted upon cleanliness, but saw that the occupants had an adequate diet. She looked after the physical welfare of her slaves, built a church for them, taught them to read. Political leaders of that period in the South discouraged the teaching of reading to Negroes, fearing it might result in a Negro uprising. But Eliza ignored this fear. She personally taught the children on her plantations, and urged them to teach their parents. And as a result of her deep concern for them, they worked for her cheerfully, and with love.

Eliza not only possessed a happy disposition, but greatly enjoyed her work. She wrote often to her father and to her brothers in England, and because ships carrying these letters might not always reach their destination, she carefully made copies. These copies, in her own handwriting, are preserved today, and allow us to walk beside her and marvel at Eliza's many interests.

She writes of inspecting rice fields, or planting rows of tiny oak trees that "may some day be used to build a fleet." She tells of attending St. Philip's Episcopal Church in Charles Town, and of taking long walks with a Huguenot neighbor. She writes of "sending Papa a boat-load of salt beef and bacon."

Her description of three baby mocking birds that she

found on the ground is delightful. She tells of putting them in a cage at the open window of her bedroom "where mother mocking bird flies down, feeds them, and teaches them to sing." She wrote a poem about the mocking bird:

Sing on thou charming mimick of the feathered kind
And let the rational a lesson learn from thee
To mimick not defects, but harmony.

She mentions a young minister who, although ordained in the Episcopal Church, had become a Methodist. His name: the Reverend George Whitefield. Governor Oglethorpe of Georgia invited young Whitefield to his estate to evangelize the Indians and Negroes; and so well did the youthful minister succeed in this, that he crossed Georgia's border into Carolina to see whether he might have the same success in saving souls of Carolina's Indian, Negro, and even white men and women.

He used neither prayer books nor churches, but preached in open fields or by the roadside, and his stirring sermons so moved his listeners that Charles Town's religious leaders resented his activities. He was arrested, brought to trial, and found guilty of "excesses and faults."

Eliza wrote to her father of the Charles Town trial, which created intense excitement. She sympathized with the young man whose methods were not unlike those of another, long ago, preaching a Sermon on the Mount.

Perhaps the trial helped to strengthen her belief in religious toleration. Many settlers had come to the New World for religious freedom, and Eliza's Huguenot neighbor told her about the French Huguenots, meeting in caves, tortured to death if discovered. The Huguenots had their own church in Charles Town and were given respect. Why had not young

George Whitefield received this same toleration? The answer to this question eluded her.

About this time, Eliza's father sent indigo seeds to Eliza from Antigua, and instructed her in careful preparation of the soil for their planting, and care of the young plants during their periods of growth. He would send a man from the West Indies when the indigo was ready to be cut and the leaves transformed into purple cakes of dye for market.

She placed some of the indigo seeds on the palm of her small hand and studied them. She'd do her best to follow Papa's instructions, and she hoped the seeds would grow.

Little did she realize the potential magic in her hand. Little did she foresee, looking at the seeds, that fleets of ships, laden with indigo, would one day sail from Carolina and return with gold. How could she know that, because of her work with indigo, many a Carolina-born young man would be Oxford educated; would come home from England to play an important part in America's history?

Eliza's first field of indigo was touched by early frost. She planted a second and third without success. At last, after getting more seed from her father, the fourth field showed such promise that she wrote: "Papa, please send me the man now. I must learn to prepare indigo for market."

Mr. Lucas sent a man named Cromwell. He came from the French island of Montserrat in the West Indies.

Eliza watched Cromwell's every move as he directed the Negroes in the building of huge vats, in laying indigo leaves in some of these vats and covering the leaves with water.

"They must soak until they begin to ferment, but not too much," he told Eliza. "Their color must be exactly right."

She remained at his side and begrudged time for eating and sleeping. She watched him draw the purple liquid into empty vats, then instruct the Negroes to beat the liquid with paddles until it thickened. He allowed the thick liquid to settle, then drew off all the water. The remaining sediment, resembling purple fudge, was cut into small squares.

But the squares, Cromwell told Eliza, were of inferior quality and not commercial indigo. She looked up into his face, but he could not meet her eyes.

She knew that his own island of Montserrat exported indigo in large quantities. Had he deliberately ruined her indigo, rather than help create in Carolina an indigo market that would compete some day with his own?

He said: "It's Carolina's climate. You'll never grow first class indigo here."

Eliza did not argue with him. She sent the man back to the West Indies, and wrote her father the whole story. "Please let me have another man, Papa," she pleaded. "This time, an *honest* one!"

In a few months, another came. He taught Eliza the true technique of making indigo. In time she grew so proficient that she was able to export great quantities to England; and finally England offered a bounty of sixpence a pound for Carolina indigo, thus shutting off the French product from British markets.

It was characteristic of Eliza that she offered packages of indigo seeds to many Carolina planters, and actually devoted her entire 1744 crop to this purpose. The other planters became successful growers and exporters of indigo, their profits building schools, churches, beautiful Charles Town homes.

Now Major Lucas had been promoted to Lieutenant Colonel and had become Antigua's governor. He decided that the time had come to take a hand in Eliza's matrimonial future, and he wrote her a long letter describing two eligible men in the West Indies. "One is an old gentleman of great wealth," he wrote, "and the other a young man possessing many qualities necessary in a good husband. At your age, Eliza, it is well to think of marriage."

Eliza, who prided herself upon being a dutiful and affectionate daughter, became greatly upset by this letter. She had built a personal world that held immense promise, here in Carolina. The very thought of going to Antigua, or marrying either a wealthy old gentleman, or a young one, filled her heart with dread.

Colonel Pinckney and Mrs. Pinckney had recently sent her an urgent invitation to spend a few days with them at Belmont, and she now accepted, eager to talk over her problem with someone whose advice she valued highly. No use discussing the matter with Mama, who would no doubt consider Papa's scheme both prudent and practical.

She was welcomed joyously at Belmont by Colonel and Mrs. Pinckney, and during luncheon talked with them of such unimportant matters as the price of tea, latest Paris hoopskirts, Richardson's new best selling novel, *Pamela*. Eliza felt Colonel Pinckney's glance now and then, and his eyes told her he knew that beneath her light conversation there was a note of apprehension and concern. After luncheon he suggested that they all go out and look at two young colts in the stable.

"I'll stay here and finish *Pamela*," said Mrs. Pinckney, who was still confined to her wheel chair. "You two go."

After inspecting the colts, Eliza and the Colonel walked along a shady path to a bench he called his favorite retreat, and he sat down, motioning her beside him.

"At the edge of the woods here," he said, "I'm reminded of long-ago Indians who had no problems but those of clothing, shelter and food."

"How do we know?" Eliza asked. "Many an Indian girl may have resented her father's determination to arrange a marriage for her. She perhaps abhorred her father's choice."

He looked at her. "Eliza, what's troubling you? Out with it."

She stared in silence a moment at the live oak trees wearing their lacy scarves of Spanish moss. The perfume of myrtle and jasmine came to her, reminding Eliza that this dear land was now part of her. *She could not leave it.*

She said: "Papa wants to arrange a marriage for me in Antigua. He has picked out two possible suitors."

He did not speak. She glanced at last into his face. He had grown stern and pale.

She said, her heart beating quickly: "Should I go?"

He said: "I was born in Carolina. I love every leaf and blade of grass. *But your going would turn it for me into a wilderness.*"

She caught her breath. The world suddenly grew so beautiful she could not look at it. She closed her eyes a moment.

Presently they got up and went back to the house, where Mrs. Pinckney greeted them with a smile. She put a finger in the book she was reading, to keep the place.

"You must read this, Eliza," she said. "Pamela was quite a girl."

"I will," Eliza promised. "But if you'll excuse me now, I'll run up to my bedroom and write a letter to Papa."

Mrs. Pinckney did not mind. Eliza must regard Belmont as her home, during this visit. And would she please give her best wishes to Lieutenant Colonel Lucas?

Eliza nodded, and hurried upstairs. She went into her bedroom, closed the door and sat down at the desk. She took pen and paper and wrote to her father that as she was only eighteen, she hoped he would put aside the thought of marriage for her. At least for two or three years. "I promise to indulge in no passion for anyone unless you approve," she wrote. "But I do not wish to marry either of the men you describe, Papa. *Not for all the riches of Chile and Peru.*"

During the next few days Eliza enjoyed her stay at Belmont, and Mrs. Pinckney enjoyed having her young guest. She even went so far as to tell Eliza that if "anything happened" she would be willing to let Eliza take her place. Eliza, bending to kiss her hostess, assured her that no one had ever paid her such a generous compliment, but "nothing would happen." Mrs. Pinckney must believe that she would get better, and walk again, too.

One day, in the garden where Eliza and Colonel Pinckney were admiring an exceptionally beautiful rose, she said:

"I wrote Papa and begged him to put aside all thought of marriage for me, at least for two or three years. I promised I'd indulge in no passion for anyone, unless he approved."

Colonel Pinckney did not smile. He asked: "You think love waits for approval?" He waited for her answer, but she remained silent, and he added: "When you're my age you'll know that disapproval has no more effect upon love than have snowflakes upon sunshine."

She picked a rosebud, slipped it through a brooch at the throat of her white dress. Yes, he was twenty years older than she, but she was never conscious of the difference in their age. Never.

"I've half decided," she said, "to become an old maid."

His eyes met hers, smiling. "At eighteen? Well, I'm glad you've only *half* decided. Not completely. There's still hope."

She laughed, and they walked out of the garden toward a spreading tree beneath which sat Mrs. Pinckney, reading in her wheel chair.

During the next two years, Eliza visited Belmont frequently; and at home, on her three plantations, her daily hours brimmed with projects and plans. Indigo was thriving and had a good market. Rice crops had been good, but the price of rice had declined. Her cotton fields produced abundantly but the cotton gin had not yet been invented and this crop was not too profitable.

The Colonel had continued to lend Eliza books from his library, and now she was deeply interested in the writings of John Locke (1632-1704) who made various logical, daring statements. Locke declared that the state's highest function was to protect life, liberty and property of its citizens; and when these natural rights were trampled upon by political authority, the people themselves had a *right and duty* to rebel and make a change in their government.

While reading John Locke at the age of twenty, in 1743, Eliza could not foresee that one day his words would touch off the American Revolution and help formulate our Declaration of Independence. Not only did she agree with his theories of government, education, and religious toleration, but she promised herself that if she ever had children of her own, she'd do her best to instill in them Locke's philosophy.

Early in January, 1744, Eliza received a letter from her father that filled her with dismay and alarm. He wrote that he was sending her brother, George Lucas, to Carolina to bring Eliza, Polly and their mother to the West Indies. George would soon be leaving for Carolina.

It meant that Eliza must abandon all present projects that she'd begun on the plantations and tear herself away from this dear land. How could she do it? To a dutiful daughter, her father's word was law, but surely, *surely* she would think of some escape.

Mrs. Lucas was delighted at the prospect of an exciting ocean trip. And she'd be with her husband again! To Polly it seemed romantic beyond belief. The very thought of going to Antigua made the young girl dance with joy.

Although Eliza tried to school herself to "endeavor cheerfully to resign to the Divine," this was too much. It was not to be borne. Yes, an intelligent person submitted to the inevitable, but one must always make sure that it *was* inevitable, that no escape was possible.

How to avoid going? She knew Papa would not allow her to stay alone, here in Carolina. Yes, she was twenty-one, therefore an adult; but until her marriage, Papa would be lord and master and she must obey. This was the eighteenth century.

A few days after the receipt of her father's letter, Eliza learned of the sudden death of Mrs. Pinckney. She attended the funeral. His wife's death left Colonel Pinckney quite alone, except for servants, at Belmont.

He and Mrs. Pinckney had had no children.

George arrived from Antigua. Eliza had not seen him for six years, and he had grown to manhood. She showed him over the plantations, and pointed out her proud projects such as the indigo and the thriving young oaks.

He noticed her lack of appetite and the sadness in her eyes. He marveled at her thoughtful silence while he and Mama and Polly discussed passage on the man of war that would take them to the West Indies.

"I'll be glad to get you home to Antigua," he told Eliza. "You should be going to parties and having fun. Here, it's all work, and no play."

Eliza looked at him. How could she explain to this young brother that her work had been play? That her heart was in Carolina?

One afternoon, Colonel Pinckney called at the Lucas home. After he had paid his respects to Mrs. Lucas, and talked with George, he asked Eliza to show him through the stables. He was always interested in horses.

But when they stood together in the stable near Eliza's favorite colt, he said:

"I couldn't sleep last night, for the thought of your leaving. Eliza, my darling, don't go away. Marry me. I love you . . ."

Next moment she was in his arms. Her world had righted itself.

And so, during the days that followed, Eliza and her mother made preparations for the wedding. Ordinarily, a wedding would not take place so soon after Colonel Pinckney's first wife's death; but Eliza's mother felt that her daughter must be married before she and Polly and George sailed to Antigua.

Eliza's father not only gave his consent to the marriage, but in her diary Eliza described his wedding present as a "fortune." It saddened her that this beloved parent could not attend the wedding ceremony and walk with her up the church aisle. But as Governor, he could not leave his important work in Antigua.

On May 25, 1744, Eliza Lucas and Colonel Charles Pinckney were married. She was twenty-one, he forty-five. And theirs was perhaps the happiest marriage ever recorded.

The man of war that was to take Eliza's mother, sister and brother to Antigua did not arrive. Eliza and her new husband lived at the Wappoo plantation until passage could be booked for Mrs. Lucas, Polly and George on a brig. Mrs. Lucas was upset at the thought of making the trip upon this type of ship instead of the promised man of war, but when departure day came, she and her family boarded the brig and waved goodbye to Eliza and Colonel Pinckney. As she stood on the wharf, watching the ship sail away, Eliza was unaware of the fact that she and her mother were never to meet again.

After the family had gone, Eliza moved with her husband to Belmont, but continued to supervise her father's three plantations and to write him many letters. As always, she made copies of these letters; and today we may read in them her love for Colonel Pinckney. She mentions again and again his "good nature, sweetness of temper, generous heart." She wrote: "My deepest inclination is to please my husband, even in trifles."

Belmont, their "country house," was five miles from town, but in Charles Town itself Colonel Pinckney owned "Mansion House" which occupied a square of land and afforded an unobstructed view of Charles Town's harbor. This house, two stories high, built of small dark English brick, had kitchen and offices in the basement. Behind the house were cabins for servants, also stables, and a fine vegetable garden; but beyond all this was a miniature park with rare shade trees and colorful flower beds.

At Mansion House, Eliza's first child was born, a healthy little boy, on February 25, 1746. He had Colonel Pinckney's dark eyes and was christened Charles Cotesworth Pinckney. He was to play a vital role in America's history.

Eliza entered upon the career of motherhood with joyous enthusiasm and letters to her father were filled with descriptions of the baby. When he was three months old, she wrote: "I think I can already discover in him his father's good sense, sincere and generous mind, sweetness of disposition." To a friend in England she wrote to ask for a toy that would teach young Charles his letters by the time he could speak. She explained: "According to John Locke, he can play himself into learning."

John Locke walked beside Eliza during every hour of her child's training. Before Charles Cotesworth was two years old he could "tell all the letters in any book." When he grew older, she insisted that he must not merely learn by rote. John Locke had pointed out that this was wrong. "True learning," Locke had said, "is a *search for evidence.*"

Eliza and Colonel Pinckney found great joy, always, in each other's companionship. To them, marriage was a "never ending, interesting conversation." They took long walks together in Charles Town. They enjoyed the plays in Dock Street Theatre, attended St. Philip's Episcopal Church, walked by the Old Powder Magazine, and sometimes paused to watch slaves being sold in the Slave Market. They'd stroll along the wharf and stop to look at indigo being loaded upon ships.

Indigo daily brought wealth to Carolina. Planters could double their capital every three years growing indigo, and a million pounds was now exported annually.

In 1747, when Eliza was expecting a second child, word came of her father's death in Antigua. Her grief was very deep, because her father had always seemed as much a part of her as life itself. Her child was born dead.

But next year, on August 8, 1748, Eliza's little daughter, Harriott, was born. Two years later, on October 23, 1750, she had a second son and he was christened Thomas. Now her family was complete. And it seemed to Eliza that she had all the blessings God could possibly bestow. If the Good Fairy should pause beside her and ask her to make the three traditional wishes, she'd not be able to comply. She had everything.

Although Eliza was unaware at this time of his existence, a young man was now growing up on a farm in the next colony, Virginia. In 1750 he'd just celebrated his eighteenth birthday, and one of his favorite studies was the science of military strategy. His name: George Washington. Many years later, he and Eliza would meet, and his military career would have a profound effect upon her own life.

Colonel Pinckney practiced law in Charles Town until the death of his close friend, Chief Justice Graeme. Upon his friend's death, his title, Chief Justice, was bestowed upon Colonel Pinckney by Carolina's Governor. Eliza shared this honor with deep pride, and for a year after her husband's appointment as Chief Justice of the Colony, Colonel Pinckney performed his duties faithfully. At the end of the year he was stunned to learn that King George of England, instead of confirming his appointment, had given the title of Chief Justice of the Colony to a Mr. Peter Leigh.

It was a blow. Eliza tried to make light of it, but Colonel Pinckney was shocked and hurt. What did King George II know about Colonel Pinckney's fine record, his fitness for the position? After all, the King was three thousand miles away.

In March, 1753, Colonel Pinckney was appointed Commissioner of the Colony in London. He decided to accept. Thus when young Thomas was three, Harriott five, Charles Cotesworth seven, the Pinckney's set sail for England.

It was a stormy, uncomfortable voyage of twenty-five days, during which Eliza, her husband, and all their children were seasick. She had the feeding and care of three cages of Carolina birds they'd brought along; an indigo bird, a nonpareil, and a yellow bird. All three, by a small miracle, survived the trip.

In England, they journeyed to Richmond and rented a house. And soon after arrival, Eliza called upon the Princess of Wales and her nine children, taking the three birds along as a gift. The Princess, delighted with the birds, also fell in love with little Harriott Pinckney and took the child on her knee. She laughed and talked with her, and little Harriott was soon at home with this "nice lady." The Princess and Eliza discussed their views on the growth and development of children, and had much in common as to ideas on discipline and education. The Royal children, their mother admitted, were sometimes naughty. Eliza received this news without surprise.

Eliza wrote to a Carolina friend about this meeting with the Princess of Wales. "She introduced her eldest son to me. One day, of course this young man will become England's King George III."

It is interesting to read Eliza's letters that describe London in 1754. "There is a housing shortage," she writes. "We searched and searched for a house in London, but could not find one from Temple Bar to Charing Cross." Later the Pinckneys found a house, and she wrote: "Now we attend London balls and parties. And we never miss a play when Garrick is to act."

Carolina friends wrote about the war between the British and French Colonies in America. The French were occupying Fort Duquesne (now Pittsburg) in 1754; and twenty-one year old George Washington was sent with troops by Virginia's governor to resist that occupation. Washington was defeated, and news of this greatly alarmed Colonel Pinckney and Eliza. They agreed with Benjamin Franklin, who had recently said: "The English Colonies will never know rest while the French are masters of Canada."

The next year the British Government sent General Braddock to Virginia with two regiments. With Washington as his aide, Braddock led British and Provincial troops toward Fort Duquesne, marching with greatest difficulty through unbroken wilderness. Axemen cleared, ahead of their march, a twelve foot wagon road. When Braddock and Washington reached a point five miles from Fort Duquesne, the French sent two hundred soldiers and six hundred war-painted Indians who concealed themselves in high grass and behind trees, then attacked the British, mortally wounding Braddock. This left young Washington in command. During Washington's forced retreat to Virginia, Braddock died.

News of all this reached Eliza and the Colonel in London, disturbing them greatly. They also learned that the Governors of all the Colonies had met, at Benjamin Franklin's suggestion, to plan united action against the French and their Indian rallies. "Union is Strength" was the motto of this meeting, a motto later to lay a foundation for defiance of the British Empire.

Colonel and Eliza Pinckney decided to sail back to Carolina, taking with them their little daughter, Harriott, but leaving Tom and Charles Cotesworth, age eight and ten, in school in London. They boarded a ship in March, 1758, and because England and France had now declared war, the crossing was extremely dangerous, and they did not reach Carolina until the 19th of May.

Colonel Pinckney, after his absence of five years, found that the plantations were badly in need of attention. He began to travel from one to the other, giving himself no rest. This strenuous work, soon after the difficult trip from England, overtaxed his strength and he became ill, with a high fever. On July 12th, he died.

Eliza's intense grief, after fourteen happy years of marriage, was heartbreaking to behold. She wrote: "Even his poor slaves traveled some thirty or forty miles in the night to see the last of a Master they adored." For many days after the funeral she was too stunned for tears.

But gradually, life forced itself upon her. There was the care of her little daughter, the supervision of their property. She took up her work again.

Belmont had "gone back to the woods," she wrote in her

diary. She arose early each morning, worked every daylight hour, and finally restored Belmont, and her own plantations, to their former efficient and immaculate condition.

She had supervision of three hundred Negroes. She was responsible for the growing of their food, making of all their clothing, the care of their sick, the education of their children.

Money from indigo was still building fine Carolina homes and sending young men to Oxford and Cambridge. Neighboring colonies were growing indigo and sharing in its profits.

Britain's capture of Quebec on September 8, 1789, and the Treaty of Paris, three years later, ended French rule in North America. Eliza could look ahead to an era of great prosperity.

Her sons were doing well at school in England, and she frequently sent the school a barrel of rice. She wrote to the school's housekeeper: "My boys like the rice boiled dry. They eat it with their meat instead of bread."

George III became England's king in 1760. And five years later, the British Government decided that the Colonies should help pay for the recent war. The Stamp Act was passed. Expensive stamps were to be placed upon newspapers, legal documents, bonds, leases, etc. Proceeds from the sale of these must be sent to England.

The expensive new stamps were burned in the streets, from Massachusetts to South Carolina. Flags were flown at half mast, and shops were closed. Eliza's sons, at their school in England, surprised classmates and teachers by standing up and "declaring vehemently" against the Stamp Act.

The next year, the Stamp Act was repealed. Peace settled over the colonies.

It was an uneasy peace, but it allowed Eliza to concentrate

upon her plantations, and her home and family. In 1768, her daughter Harriott, now nineteen, married a thirty-five year old widower, Daniel Horry.

After nineteen years spent in England, Eliza's two sons returned to Charles Town and began to practise law. They were Oxford graduates and had studied Military Science at the Royal Academy in Caen, Normandy. After Charles Cotesworth's marriage to Sarah Middleton, he and his bride went to live at the Mansion House in Charles Town. Colonel Charles Pinckney had bequeathed the Mansion House to his elder son.

The Colonies of course had no part in the election of members of the British Parliament, but the British imposed upon the Colonies "taxation without representation" in the form of a tax on tea. Eliza remembered John Locke's words: "No man has a right to that which another man has a right to take from him." She soon learned of the Boston Tea Party, and she watched Charles Town's citizens toss tons of tea into the Cooper River.

Eliza's plantations were making money. Great quantities of rice and indigo from these plantations were being shipped to England. Her two sons visited her frequently, and life was very pleasant in spite of warning of war clouds upon the horizon.

She had written to her sons every single week during all the years they'd spent at school in England, and this correspondence had kept her close to them, and kept them close to her. The young men, Charles Cotesworth and Thomas Pinckney, quoted John Locke as often as did their mother, and Eliza listened, fascinated, while Charles Cotesworth spoke emphatically about the necessity for separation of Church and State, and about religious toleration. Religious toleration?

Eliza's memory went back to the Reverend George White-field in Charles Town's courtroom. How many years ago? Thirty!

At the age of fifty, Eliza's hair had turned a little gray. Fine lines fanned from the corners of her very blue eyes. But each morning she still arose at five, she scheduled her daily hours, and often read a book till midnight.

Her elder son was always called Charles Cotesworth, rather than just "Charles." This distinguished him from his cousin, Charles Pinckney, now a boy of fifteen.

Without benefit of radio, telephone, or even trains, news in 1774 traveled slowly. In due time, however, Eliza learned of the meeting on September 5th of fifty-one delegates from the Colonies, in Philadelphia, George Washington among them. They voted to stop British imports and to support Massachusetts if British force was used against the Colony. They sent to King George III a *Declaration of Rights and Grievances*.

Eliza remembered the Princess of Wales, mother of King George III. Perhaps she would advise her son against war with the Colonies. But George III wrote: "The die is cast, the Colonies must either submit or triumph!" Eliza knew, of course, that Carolina, with its vast export of rice and indigo, would now face financial ruin. But she knew also that war was inevitable.

On the night of April 18, 1775, the British commander at Boston, General Gage, ordered his men to confiscate military supplies stored at Concord, twenty miles from Boston; and to stop at Lexington and arrest John Hancock and Samuel Adams. It is history that Paul Revere warned Lexington citizens, and that armed colonists (minute men) met the British and fired the first shot for American independence, the "shot heard round the world." John Hancock and Samuel Adams managed to escape.

Eliza, from Carolina, wrote to a friend: "the tents are on the green." Her sons exchanged their courtroom robes for uniforms. Both had been made captains.

The Continental Army's Commander, George Washington, ordered Eliza's sons to James Island in Charles Town's harbor. And on June 28, 1776, Charles Town was bombarded for ten terrifying hours by the British fleet. Eliza watched the battle from Belmont, praying that her sons' lives might be saved; and when the British finally sailed away, defeated, she felt "the most intense relief of her life."

Next month the Declaration of Independence alerted all thirteen Colonies to arm against Britain. The Declaration was read from every pulpit and public platform in Charles Town; bells rang, guns were fired. Every loyal citizen rejoiced that a new country had been formed: the United States of America.

During the next three years, Charles Town itself was out of the direct line of battle, but Eliza, with her two sons serving under General Washington, accompanied them, in imagination, during every step of the war. She suffered with them as they retreated in defeat from New York. She accompanied them in spirit while Washington's depleted, starving army crossed the Delaware on December 8, 1776.

Washington's plan to re-cross the Delaware on Christmas night resulted in victory at Trenton and later at Princeton. Eliza read, with immense pride, that in far-away Prussia, Frederick the Great declared that the Trenton and Princeton victories were *"the most brilliant in the annals of warfare."*

A new flag was adopted on June 14, 1777: the stars and stripes. And in October of that year the British General Burgoyne surrendered with 6000 men at Saratoga.

A week before Burgoyne's surrender, Washington had lost to the British at Brandywine Creek, near Philadelphia; and the British captured that city. A second defeat, at Germantown, caused Washington to withdraw to Valley Forge, twenty miles northeast of Philadelphia, where he and his men went into winter quarters. All students of American history know of the sufferings of Washington and his men at Valley Forge during that terrible winter, without sufficient food, with men's bare feet leaving bloody prints in the snow. Eliza, reading of this afterward, wept.

In 1778, France signed a treaty of aid to the thirteen Colonies and many young Frenchmen, including the Marquis de Lafayette, offered their services to George Washington. But in December of that year, the British captured Georgia.

Carolina might be next!

Thomas, Eliza's younger son, who had recently married Elizabeth Mott, advised his mother to hide the family valuables on his Carolina plantation, the "Ashepoo." Eliza, taking his advice, ordered all family papers, jewels, rare china, paintings and money, to be stored in the cellar of the Ashepoo house.

In March, 1779, came the frightening news that the British General Provost, with 3000 men, was marching toward Charles Town and laying waste the entire countryside. Eliza locked all the doors at Belmont and remained inside while Provost and his troops surrounded her house. Three British soldiers began to put the torch to Belmont. Eliza escaped with her life.

Then Provost and his men marched to the Ashepoo plantation and applied the torch to the house and all its priceless contents. Not a jewel, not a valuable paper, a painting, nor any of the money, was saved.

Eliza, traveling at night, her journey crowded with danger,

finally reached the home of her daughter on the Hampton estate forty miles from Charles Town. She remained hidden during daylight hours, but was able to watch the activities of the British at various plantations. She saw them take away the Negro men and women, leave the children, confiscate the horses, slaughter the livestock.

When Charles Cotesworth Pinckney, now a Colonel, learned of his mother's great financial loss at Ashepoo, he offered her half of all his money and possessions. She refused to accept anything. "Don't grieve for me, my dear son," she said. "God forbid I should think my lot hard while I have such children."

Both Charles Cotesworth and Thomas fought in the battle of Stono, near Charles Town, and helped defeat General Provost, who retreated to Savannah. But Charles Town was still in great danger; and in the spring Sir Henry Clinton and Lord Cornwallis marched troops overland from Savannah and surrounded Charles Town itself.

For a horrifying month, British shells rained upon Charles Town. Women and children were shot down in the streets. Finally, on May 12, 1780, Charles Town surrendered; Clinton and Cornwallis with 8000 British soldiers marched in.

Thomas Pinckney managed to escape. He joined George Washington's army. Charles Cotesworth, taken prisoner, was confined on a farm just outside Charles Town. Eliza was living with her daughter at Hampton.

Sir Henry Clinton returned to New York, leaving Lord Cornwallis in Charles Town with five thousand "red coats." These young British soldiers, quartered in the city's finest homes, lived well; the owners of the homes lived in the garrets. Mothers hid pretty daughters from the enemy, and one mother kept secret the presence in the attic of three young girls to whom she took food at night.

Five thousand healthy young soldiers, far from home, demanded entertainment. British redcoats gave balls and parties, and ordered the attractive young ladies of Charles Town to attend. Wearing their loveliest gowns, the Southern girls danced with handsome British officers and soldiers, but being "true patriots" did not fall in love. At least, not openly. A girl suspected of being interested in a redcoat faced the biting scorn of her family and friends.

At Hampton, Eliza was secretly visited by Francis Marion, Thomas Sumper and Andrew Pickens, prominent leaders of the Revolution. They told her news of her sons, and of the outside world. She learned that Thomas had been severely wounded. And that General Benedict Arnold had turned traitor and fled to the British lines.

The British occupied Charles Town for two and one-half years. During all this time, Eliza suffered great poverty, as well as actual hunger. She had no home. She wrote in her journal: "Even a little hovel I built for one of my Negroes, which would now be of great service to me, has been confiscated." She remained at her daughter's home, but starvation was never far from that door.

Suddenly, Lord Cornwallis marched away, with his men, leaving a British officer in charge of Charles Town. Cornwallis took up a position in Yorktown, Virginia, and almost immediately young Lafayette stationed his soldiers in front of Yorktown, at Malvery Hill. Eliza's sons had managed to rejoin General Washington, and Washington's army arrived at a point outside Yorktown. *Cornwallis was surrounded.*

Just as Charles Town had been bombarded, the American artillery dropped shells, day after day, upon Yorktown. On October 17, 1781, Cornwallis hoisted the white flag. Two days later, he and his entire army surrendered and the Revolutionary War was practically over.

In December the British sailed away from Charles Town and the "ragged regimentals" marched in. Eliza, standing on the street, watching the ragged American soldiers, her sons among them, felt her heart swell with the fine sweet pride of freedom.

Eliza was now fifty-eight. Her daughter had become a widow, so Eliza decided to live at Hampton and help bring up her daughter's little girl.

Charles Cotesworth had become a widower with three small daughters whom he sent to his mother at Hampton. "No one on earth," he said, "could better prepare them for life."

The three million people now living in the United States needed a Constitution. In 1787, delegates were sent from various States to Philadelphia to prepare such a document. South Carolina sent Charles Cotesworth Pinckney.

Thomas Pinckney, now living in Charleston, became South Carolina's Governor. (In 1783, the city's name had been changed from Charles Town to Charleston.)

The war had been over for six years when Charles Cotesworth left for Philadelphia, and South Carolina had already begun to enjoy a peaceful prosperity, with flourishing plantations of indigo and cotton. Newly built white-columned mansions were springing up, and the older houses, damaged by war, were restored. Charleston's excellent newspaper, the *South Carolina Gazette*, advertised the names of local cabinetmakers who, on short notice, could make "mahogany tables, chairs, chests of drawers, bookcases, clockcases, walkingsticks."

Now Eliza wrote in one of her letters: "I regret no pleasure that I can't enjoy and I enjoy some pleasures that I could not have had at an earlier period of my life." Robert Browning had not yet been born, but here, in almost his exact words, was Browning's own philosophy of old age.

A Recipe Book written by Eliza Lucas Pinckney has been preserved and today makes delightful reading. It contains cookery recipes and cures for sore throat, inflamed eyes, thin hair, and other troubles that vexed human beings of her era, as well as human beings of our own era.

Permission to reprint the following was obtained from the *National Society of the Colonial Dames of America in the State of South Carolina:*

> For a Toothache: take a jugg of water and put a few red hott coals into it and wash the mouth often with it.
>
> To Keep Artichokes all the Year: Put them in a barrel and lay every layer with Sand that the leaves do not touch one another, then bury them about one foot in the ground.
>
> To Make Little Cakes for Tea: Of butter, flour, sugar, a quarter of a pound each; and then as much yolk of egg as will mix it into a stiff Paste. Make them into round cakes and bake them on tinns; about the size of a half-crown; put some caraway seeds in them.

One imagines Eliza and her daughter eating these little cakes at tea, talking of Charles Cotesworth at Constitutional Convention in Philadelphia. Charles Pinckney, his cousin, had gone with him; and the two Pinckneys, with fifty-three other delegates, were creating the document that would serve Americans down through the coming centuries.

After four months of work on the Constitution, Charles Cotesworth Pinckney came home from Philadelphia and gave his mother a report of the Convention. Yes, he told her, the delegates had signed the completed document. Now the Constitution would be submitted to the States for ratification.

He and his mother sat in the living room at Hampton, and

as Eliza looked at him she could not help thinking how much he resembled his father. Charles Cotesworth had Colonel Pinckney's stalwart build, compelling dark eyes, and his same "passion for the public good."

"Did anyone take a day-to-day transcript of the work of the Convention?" Eliza asked.

"No, mother. But in the evening some of the delegates wrote of the day's happenings and proceedings in their personal diaries."

"Did you make many speeches?" she asked.

"Not many. But I did insist upon the inclusion of religious freedom. I wasn't the only delegate who spoke for that, but *I was one,* and I argued for it as strongly as I could. I did help to make sure that no religious test should be required as a qualification to any office or public trust under the United States."

Eliza, sitting forward in her chair, listening intently, could not speak for a moment, because of the proud swelling of her heart. Her thoughts hurried back to the day when her dear husband had given her a book by John Locke.

It was wonderful to be the mother of a son like Charles Cotesworth. It was wonderful to know that the Constitution would always bear a small imprint of your teaching.

When her son had left, Eliza sat alone, thinking of her husband. If only he might be here today!

The Constitution was adopted and George Washington elected President in 1789. During his second term of office, President Washington toured the South, and drove several miles out of his way to have breakfast at Hampton with Eliza and her daughter. He told Eliza that although her two sons had given much to their country, her sons' contribution did not surpass her own.

In the Spring of 1793, Eliza became so ill that Charleston

doctors advised her to consult a noted surgeon in Philadelphia. She and her daughter left by ship from Charleston Harbor, and after ten rough sailing days arrived in Philadelphia, where they rented an apartment.

President Washington immediately called upon Eliza, offering the use of his carriage, arranging for her every comfort. At first the noted surgeon was able to relieve her pain, but she suddenly grew worse. On May 26, 1793, Eliza Lucas Pinckney died.

She was buried in St. Peter's churchyard in Philadelphia. It is said that, at his own request, President George Washington helped carry her casket to its final resting place.

Such was the life of Eliza Lucas Pinckney, the Southern girl who believed that all worthwhile success must be paid for in advance by self-denial. She paid gladly.

We who today enjoy the America she helped to build, are deeply in her debt.

4

SUSAN B. ANTHONY
(1820-1906)

Daniel Anthony was twenty-six when his wife, Lucy, gave birth to their second child on February 15, 1820. Just before the baby came, he found it difficult to remain calm and serene as should a young Quaker father, according to Quaker rule. His wife's mother, Susannah Read, was in the bedroom with Lucy, and Daniel longed to go in there to share with his wife this momentous moment. But custom restrained him.

He walked into the living room and began to read a geneology of the Anthony family. William Anthony had left Germany in 1515 and made his home in England. John Anthony, William's grandson, had sailed to America from England in 1634. The geneology went on to say that John's son, living in Rhode Island, became a Quaker. All very interesting, but Daniel's mind was upon Lucy, and he put the geneology down and went out on the front porch.

The Savoy Road that ran by his house and connected this small town of Adams, Massachusetts, with Boston, was white with winter snow, and quite empty. The snowy hills surrounding Adams were empty, too, as was the vast expanse of cloudy sky. Daniel wished that his little two year old daughter, Guelma, had not been sent to a neighbor's today. He felt completely lonely.

But just then his ear caught a new sound. An infant's cry. He turned and ran into the house.

Moments later, his wife's mother came from the bedroom with a baby wrapped in a white blanket, and she laid it in Daniel's arms.

She said, smiling: "A perfect little girl." She hurried back to Lucy.

Daniel Anthony, glancing into the face of his new daughter, felt his heart beat swiftly. Did he sense that with her coming he would never be lonely again? Did he somehow realize that here was someone who'd grow up to make him famous because he was her father?

He continued to gaze at her, reluctant to break the spell of seeing her for the first time, holding her tenderly against his black Quaker coat. He had no way of predicting that this small being would one day, by applying the torch of truth to tradition's fetters, free for a new-way-of-life all the women of the world.

At last he carried the baby into the bedroom and laid her down beside his wife, Lucy, on the bed.

Lucy smiled up at him from the pillow. "The baby has your eyes, Daniel. And your firm chin. What shall we name her?"

He said: "Let's name her Susan Brownell, for my sister."

Lucy turned her head to look at the new baby. "Susan Brownell Anthony. A big name. But she may grow up to it."

Old Father Time, if watching, would have been amused. Grow up to it? There's no doubt that she *did*.

Susan B. Anthony's childhood was happy, due in part to her wise choice of parents. Daniel was a good business man who provided well for his family, which eventually consisted of five girls and two boys. Susan's mother, who had not been a Quaker before her marriage to Daniel, lavished upon her children all the devoted service of which she was capable.

Susan learned to read at the age of three, and from then on no book in the Anthony home was safe from her curiosity. Daniel encouraged her in every way. He was building a cotton mill, making frequent trips to New York City, and Susan always waited longingly for his return, not for "what he might bring her" but for the joy of climbing on his knee and getting help with difficult passages in some new book. Never was Daniel too busy. Never did he refuse to share with Susan his most precious possession: *time*.

When Susan was five, her older sister, Guelma, was seven. Hannah, her younger sister, was four. Their mother made them a "rag baby," a doll that afforded them more pleasure than children often receive from a dozen toys. Candy was unknown, but Susannah (Grandma Read) kept a huge tub of maple sugar and let the children feast from it. She made them hasty pudding and filled it with fresh butter and honey, a treat that Susan was to remember even when she'd grown famous and had sampled delicacies concocted by the world's great chefs.

Susan was six and her baby brother, Daniel Read Anthony, was two, when her father decided to move his family to Battenville, New York, and there build a cotton factory. Battenville was forty-four miles from Adams, but in 1826 this was such a momentous journey that when the children and their parents had finally mounted the green lumber wagon containing the family goods, and Daniel whipped up the horses, the four weeping grandparents waved good-bye. The children threw tearful kisses. Forty-four miles! Would they ever meet again?

But eight years later, fourteen-year-old Susan felt that

Battenville had always been home. At the back of their spacious brick house, Daniel had built a schoolroom; and there, under a competent teacher, Susan, Guelma, Hannah, young Daniel Read, and seven-year-old Mary, spent daily hours. Susan's small sister, Eliza, had died at the age of two; and Jacob Merritt, the youngest, was still a babe. Grandmother and Grandfather Read had come to live with them, and Daniel's cotton factory was thriving.

Daniel Anthony refused to buy for his factory any raw cotton produced by slave labor. He was also a Temperance advocate and often spoke of "the evils of drink." Susan, worshipping her remarkable father, adopted wholeheartedly both his Temperance and anti-slavery philosophy.

Susan learned to cook and "sew a fine seam." She could make delicious bread and biscuits. "Thee will have no trouble finding a husband," teased her sister, Guelma. "What man wouldn't marry thee, Susan, for such cooking?"

Susan always laughed at this, but secretly she wondered about marriage. Her mother's endless household drudgery was lightened by Daniel's love. But suppose Susan could not find a husband who was like her father? What of marriage *then?*

No girl of fourteen dwells long upon such thoughts, and Susan's daily leisure hours held interesting activities. In her father's factory she watched girls, no older than herself, wind cotton upon spools. She sauntered down to the blacksmith's shop and saw the horses shod. She listened while men talked with her father about the re-election of the seventh President, Andrew Jackson.

After dinner, the young Anthonys would sit with their parents in the immense living room where an open grate fire added its glow to the candlelight; and they'd beg their mother to tell them again how she, a good Baptist, had given up singing and dancing to become a Quaker's wife. She would tell them of dancing till dawn the night before her wedding while Daniel waited patiently outside the dance hall. She'd tell of his appearance before the stern Quaker elders, begging their permission to marry a girl not of their Quaker faith. The elders had given their consent. Reluctantly.

"But thou knowest I'd have married thee anyway," Daniel always said at this point in Lucy's story. "Quaker rule or no, I'd have married thee for love."

Susan felt that her mother never regretted having to forsake all worldly things for Daniel. She had been compensated by his love, and by his attitude toward her as a respected mental equal.

It was during her fourteenth year that Susan was allowed to work for two weeks in her father's factory as a "spooler." She received two dollars. And it was characteristic of her that she kept none of this money for herself, but spent half of it for some pink china cups and saucers she knew her mother wanted, and gave the other dollar to her sister, Hannah. (Today one of these pink cups is in the Los Angeles Museum and another may be seen at the Women's University, Rochester, New York.)

When Susan was fifteen, she taught small children in summer school, and her father, now wealthy, was criticized by neighbors for allowing his daughter to work for wages. "Every girl," Daniel told his critics, "should be trained for self-support." This statement, in 1835, was indeed "modern."

At the age of seventeen, Susan was sent by her father to the Deborah Moultin's Select Seminary for Females, a Quaker boarding school near Philadelphia. Guelma had been a boarder at this school for a year, and this made it less lonely for

Susan; although Miss Deborah was difficult to please and Susan, once established at the Seminary, found herself a constant target for Miss Deborah's criticism.

The criticism for such trivial matters as the way an "i" was dotted or a "t" was crossed, made Susan most unhappy. One day she asked Miss Deborah: "Why do you scold me for this, and not Guelma, when my sister has made the same mistake?" Miss Deborah had an answer. "Thy sister Guelma does the best she is capable of," she said sternly, "but thee dost not. Thee has great abilities, Susan Anthony, and I demand of thee the best of thy capacity."

Susan's two years spent under this Quaker teacher gave her the trait of thoroughness, and she was never to lose it. But so unhappy were her days at the Seminary that when Daniel Anthony went bankrupt as a result of the panic of 1839, and he could no longer afford the fee of $125 per year for each daughter's schooling at Miss Moultin's, Susan was delighted at the news that she and Guelma were to be sent home.

Wonderful to sit down again in the heart of her beloved family at mealtimes and to share in their talk and laughter. But Susan was shocked when, a few weeks later, Daniel's creditors stepped into their home and even into Daniel's factory, and sold all his possessions at auction; the cotton mill, the house itself, all the furnishings. Even the vases, the silver, the woolen blankets Lucy had brought to her marriage, as a bride, were sold to the highest bidder. Daniel's distress was described in Susan's diary: "Never in all my life did I see such agony as my father passed through during those dreadful days."

Susan realized, as she watched her mother's personal treasures being sold, that everything she owned, even her clothing, belonged legally to her husband. Was this justice? The question perched upon Susan's shoulder like a persistent moth and remained there during the years of the future. She was to ask it from lecture platforms, over and over.

Daniel rented a house in the nearby village of Hardscrabble, and Susan began to make furniture for the house, surprising even herself by her carpentry skill. She made chairs, a table, even a couch. She did housework and cooking. Entries in her diary said: "Did a large washing this morning . . . Spent today at the spinning wheel . . . Baked twenty-one loaves of bread . . . Wove three yards of carpet yesterday . . . Got my quilt out of the frame . . . The new sawmill was just raised and we had twenty men to supper." In spite of all this she felt she wasn't "self-supporting." How could she earn money?

At nineteen, Susan dropped the Quaker "thee and thou" in speaking. She dressed becomingly, had lustrous brown hair, gray eyes, good profile, a beautiful smile. Several young men, impressed with her personal charm, offered their name and worldly goods; but Susan treated these proposals of marriage almost too lightly, her thoughts upon a career of teaching, not of wifehood.

She became a teacher in a Quaker school for girls at New Rochelle, and soon after her arrival, Miss Eunice Kenyon, her Principal, fell ill. After a day of teaching, Susan slept on the floor at night beside Miss Kenyon's bed and assumed the role of nurse. Susan's diary outlines the doctor's drastic treatment: "The doctor bled Miss Kenyon, applied a blister, gave her a dose of calomel." Miss Kenyon miraculously recovered, and Susan went back to her own bedroom. For teaching, she received a salary of two dollars a week.

Next she taught in her home district, receiving two dollars and fifty cents a week, and replacing a man who had been getting ten dollars! Now she began to enjoy leisure hours, for there were picnics, parties, long drives with admirers who kept bringing up the question of marriage. She did not fall in love, perhaps because her suitors seldom measured up, in her opinion, to the many fine qualities of her beloved father.

Guelma had married Aaron McLean, and Susan often visited them in their new home, sometimes making delicious biscuits which Aaron devoured hungrily. "I'd rather see a woman make biscuits like these," he said, "than solve the knottiest problems in algebra." Susan smiled. "There is no reason," she assured him, "why *any* woman shouldn't be able to do both."

That year, in Springfield, Illinois, a young man was beginning the practice of law. It is interesting to try to imagine "what might have been" had Susan and this young man met during their youth. His name: Abraham Lincoln.

It was 1840. Queen Victoria had married her prince. Elizabeth Cady Stanton and Lucretia Mott were in London, England, attending the World Anti-Slavery Convention.

From 1840 to 1848, Susan's world was bounded by the schoolroom walls. She accepted a teaching position at Canajoharie, New York, and won high praise from the School Trustees for her teaching ability.

One imagines her standing before a large map of the United States and explaining to her pupils that when we first became a nation of thirteen states, we claimed only the land from Canada to Florida, and from the Atlantic to the Mississippi. Where did all the rest come from?

Her pupils knew, or were to discover later, that our 1803 Louisiana Purchase from France gave us Iowa, Missouri, Nebraska, North and South Dakota, Oklahoma, Montana, Arkansas, Louisiana, Minnesota, west of the Mississippi, much of Kansas, some of Colorado and Wyoming. From the Northwest Territory, ceded to us by Great Britain in 1815, we obtained Michigan, Wisconsin, Ohio, Indiana, Illinois, part of Minnesota. We acquired Florida from France in 1819, and the Republic of Texas joined our Union in 1845.

Even while Susan taught geography, the map of the United States underwent great changes. We acquired the Oregon Territory from Great Britain in 1846, and this gave us Oregon, Washington and Idaho. Then, in 1848, our war with Mexico gave us Arizona, New Mexico and California.

As Susan located for her pupils the states, north, east, south, and west, she could not foresee that she would one day visit each of these states again and again, until their towns and cities grew familiar to her as was Canajoharie's Main Street now. She could not know that citizens in these states would pelt her with rotten eggs, even with stones, when she tried to speak from platforms. But she would keep on and on. And then one day, years later, an immense audience in a big city would rise in homage as she stood before them to speak. And in a town where once she'd been pelted with stones, another audience would pelt her with rose petals.

All this was far in the future. But now, in 1848, Susan was telling herself that schoolroom walls made her feel hemmed in. She longed to serve humanity on a larger scale than teaching, but how could she do this and still earn her living?

She still remained in the classroom during the day, but, in the evenings, she began to organize in Canajoharie a society known as Daughters of Temperance. Here Susan displayed a genius for organization, an ability to work and make others work. This would one day win her world acclaim. In a speech before the "Daughters" she made a statement that might be considered the ruling theme of her life. She said: *"If we say we love the cause, and then sit at our ease, surely does our action speak the lie."*

It was 1849. Young men were leaving home for the California gold fields. Susan wrote to her father: "Oh, that I were a man, that I might go!"

Susan's father, sensing her restlessness, wrote that he'd just bought a farm near Rochester, New York. Would she come home and help him run it? He couldn't afford the luxury of giving up his job in a Rochester insurance office, but perhaps, by giving up her teaching job, she could make the farm pay.

Susan needed no second invitation to give up teaching. At the close of school, in the Spring of 1849, she left the Canajoharie Academy and hurried to the farm.

The year before, in July, 1848, the first Women's Rights Convention had met at Seneca Falls, New York. Two days later the meeting had adjourned, to meet again in Rochester. Susan's father, mother and sister Mary attended this Rochester meeting.

Daniel Anthony had been well impressed by Elizabeth Cady Stanton, whom he described as a "plump, jolly matron of thirty-three, five feet tall, mother of one or two children." She advocated votes for women. Susan should meet her.

But Susan, true to her Quaker religion, considered it wrong to support by voting any government that upheld war.

"The first Women's Rights Convention covered much more area than women's votes," Daniel told her, handing her a copy of the Twelve Resolutions and a Declaration of Sentiments they had adopted. "Mrs. Stanton declared that man-made laws, rather than Old Mother Nature, have placed women in an inferior position to men, through the centuries."

Susan looked at him seriously.

"Read what was written about the meeting in one of our newspapers," he said, handing Susan a news clipping.

She read: This bolt is the most shocking and unnatural incident ever recorded in the history of humanity: if these demands were effected it would set the world by the ears, make confusion worse confounded, demoralize and degrade from their high sphere and noble destiny women of all respectable and useful classes, and prove a monstrous injury to all mankind.

"Well," said Susan, handing back the clipping and taking a long breath, "Elizabeth Cady Stanton *would* be interesting to meet!"

But it was not until the summer of 1851 that these two women actually came face to face. A friend introduced them one afternoon when Susan happened to be in Seneca Falls, Mrs. Stanton's "home town," and Elizabeth Cady Stanton invited Susan to tea. The meeting began their famous fifty-year friendship, and opened a new world to half the human race.

In Mrs. Stanton's living room, over the tea cups, Susan heard of Elizabeth Cady Stanton's meeting with the beautiful Quakeress, Lucretia Mott, in London, in 1840, when Elizabeth was twenty-five.

"At the Anti-Slavery Convention in London," Elizabeth said, "Lucretia and I, who were delegates, were forced to sit behind a curtain because we were women. We sat there, listening to the men conducting the business of the meeting until our resentment at being shut off like this arose to the point of furious anger. We got up, went outside, and sat on the steps of the Convention Hall."

"I should have done the same thing," said Susan.

"We discussed women's rights. And a direct result of our discussion was the First Women's Rights Convention here in Seneca Falls, exactly eight years later. We demanded many rights, including the right to vote."

Susan explained her Quaker attitude toward voting, and Elizabeth did not, that day, try to make Susan change her mind. She inquired about Susan's work for Temperance, and was astonished to learn that Susan expected to collect *one hundred thousand names* upon a petition for a Prohibition Law in the State of Maine. Elizabeth promised to introduce Susan to Lucretia Mott, Lucy Stone and Horace Greeley. Amelia Bloomer was already one of Susan's friends.

The afternoon passed all too quickly, and it was dark before Susan arose to go. Elizabeth was thirty-six, Susan five years younger. They were both to live for half a century beyond that momentous day of their first conversation.

A year went by and Susan still held to her belief that women did not need the vote. And then she attended, with other Daughters of Temperance a Convention of the Sons of Temperance in Albany, N. Y. The Daughters had been invited by the Sons, and Susan assumed that she might speak to a motion. She got to her feet.

The Chairman banged his gavel. "Be seated," he told Susan. "The sisters were asked here not to speak, but to listen and learn."

Susan stared at him. She glanced across the faces of the other women, and saw that few shared her resentment, for they were placidly accepting the Chairman's verdict. Instead of sitting down, Susan walked out of the hall, and some of the more courageous Daughters followed her. In the Presbyterian Church that night, Susan organized a Women's State Temperance Society, and they voted to hold a Convention in the Spring.

The next year, in Syracuse, Susan and Amelia Bloomer were invited as Women's State Temperance Society delegates to attend a Sons of Temperance Convention, and they accepted gladly, Susan taking to the Convention her Maine Prohibition Petition containing its one hundred thousand names.

But at the door of the Convention Hall they were met by their staunch friend, the Reverend Samuel J. May.

"I'm sorry," he whispered. "The Sons have just decided that women are not welcome. I can't let you in."

Susan, smiling, pushed past him. She said: "But we *are* in."

She and Amelia sat at the back of the Hall, and the Chairman opened the meeting. But a man immediately arose.

He cried: "I demand that these females be put out!"

Susan arose and she noted that many of the men were clergymen. She began: "I wish to say . . .

She was shouted down.

"It's Women's Rights you want, not Temperance!" a man cried.

"It's Free Love they want. And Atheism!"

"And divorce!" shouted another man.

Susan held up her petition. "This," she cried, "contains one hundred thousand names."

"Names of women and children don't count!" cried a scornful gentleman.

"We were invited here," said Susan. "We're your guests."

But the turmoil heightened, and finally Susan and Amelia walked out. On the sidewalk, Amelia said:

"Susan, you've never admitted that women must first have the vote, to be heard by men. Do you see now, at last?"

Susan's fingers tightened on the Maine Petition. "Yes," she said firmly. "At last, I see."

And so it was a changed Susan who returned to her home in Rochester. Her Temperance work, she realized, had dealt with effects rather than causes. Women needed, above all else, political power; they needed *the power of the vote*. To achieve this, she would dedicate her life.

In 1853, at the age of thirty-three, Susan began the work that would fill her every waking moment for the next fifty-three years. She started by knocking upon doors up and down New York State, and explaining to women who answered their doors that women's work should lie, not only within the home, but outside, too.

In each town she hired a hall, advertised her lecture in the local newspaper, spoke before the women who came, passed a collection plate for dimes and nickels that would pay train fare to the next town. She wrote in her journal: "As I journey from town to town, I find women to be as propertyless as slaves. *They must have a purse of their own.*"

She went as often as possible to see Mrs. Stanton, and after Elizabeth's five children were in bed, Susan and Elizabeth would plan campaign talks. Elizabeth would be "audience" and Susan would stand up and rehearse a speech.

The original manuscript of the first speech Susan wrote and delivered may be seen today, in her own handwriting, in the Huntington Library, in California. It contains this sentence: "There is not a right, not a privilege in justice accorded to man, that I would have denied to woman." It goes on to say that the power of a man's subsistence is power over his will, and that by retaining his "power of the purse" man enslaves a woman's will, and degrades her pride. She emphasizes that traditional customs and laws rob woman of freedom that man has always claimed for himself.

She declared that women should "make themselves heard." But in 1853 this was a daring resolve. Women were barred from colleges. If married, they might not collect their own wages. They might not become guardians of their own children. They had three respectable avenues of self-support; teaching, sewing, domestic service.

Susan's circle of personal friends began now to enlarge. Among them were Lucy Stone, Elizabeth and Antoinette Blackwell, Margaret Fuller and Ernestine Rose.

And her crusade for Women's Rights took her down roads of incredible hardship. She trudged through snowy New

York winters to knock upon doors that, when opened, were slammed in her face by women who declared: "My husband gives me all the rights I want. Why should I need a vote?"

During speeches, men in her audience stamped their feet and drowned out Susan's words. "Woman's place," they yelled, "is in the home!"

When her purse was empty, she slept in railway stations. And when she could, by good luck, afford a hotel room, she'd have to break ice in the pitcher before pouring water into the basin for her morning sponge.

Now and then she was forced to write to her father for money. He not only gave it gladly, but added an encouraging letter. She allowed herself the luxury of a visit home about once a month, and returned to the crusade with vigor and enthusiasm after long talks with her parents.

She and Elizabeth managed to obtain ten thousand signatures upon a petition for a law granting women of New York State the right to own their own property. At Albany, the State Capital, the lawmakers glanced at the petition, listened politely to all that Susan and Elizabeth had to say about women's property rights, and then refused to act.

For the next seven years, Susan traveled through New York's sixty counties, speaking wherever two or three people, or two or three hundred people, gathered together. Horse-drawn sleighs stalled in winter snowdrifts. Trains were late. Susan wrote in her diary: "Friday morning we went to the station; no train nor hope of any. A man said he could get us to Attica in time for an evening meeting, so we paid him $5. His noble pair of grays floundered through the deepest drifts I ever saw, but that night at seven we were still fourteen miles from our destination."

Success came in 1860, when the New York Legislature passed a law granting women the control of their property and earnings, also joint guardianship with the husband of their children. Susan and Elizabeth personally congratulated each lawmaker for his admirable work in making New York a better State for women. This, they admitted in the privacy of Elizabeth's home, was a good "first step."

In 1860, the Republican Party, then six years old, nominated Abraham Lincoln and he was elected President. His party's Platform said nothing about the abolition of slavery in the United States where it already existed, but excluded slavery from the Territories. South Carolina bitterly resented this Platform, as well as the Republican victory, and on December 20, 1860, South Carolina declared itself out of the Union. A month before Lincoln's inauguration as 16th President, Georgia, Alabama, Mississippi, Louisiana and Florida seceded from the Union. All this took place at Montgomery, Alabama on February 4, 1861, and created the Confederate States of America, with Mississippi's Jefferson Davis as President.

Thus the country was already divided when President Lincoln took office on March 4, 1861, at the age of fifty-two. The Fugitive Slave Law, recently declared unconstitutional by the Supreme Court, was no longer effective.

In the South that year there were about three and one-half million Negro slaves and about four hundred thousand owners. *Seventy-five per cent of white Southerners owned no slaves at all.*

President Lincoln had been in office a month when Union troops were fired upon at Fort Sumter in Charleston's harbor by Confederate soldiers behind batteries on nearby islands. Two days later, on April 14, 1861, the Civil War began.

Texas, Virginia, Arkansas, Tennessee, North Carolina, now joined the Confederacy, making eleven states, with a total population, white and Negro, of nine million. Union states, under President Lincoln, had a total population of twenty-two million.

The Civil War crashed into Susan's Women's Rights crusade, and temporarily halted it. She and Elizabeth decided that "this was the Negro's hour." They put away their women's rights talks and began to write anti-slavery speeches.

Susan went to live on her father's farm, but she read all news of the war's progress, and discussed with her father every move. In June of 1861, the capital of the Confederate States was moved to Richmond, Virginia, and Susan read Northern newspaper headlines: "*On to Richmond!*"

On July 21st, the Union forces met defeat at the Battle of Bull Run, thirty-five miles southwest of Washington. It was a fierce battle, with many killed or wounded on each side, and a Southern General, T. J. Jackson, offered Union troops such strong resistance that he won the nickname, "Stonewall."

While the Battle of Bull Run was in progress, Colonel Ulysses S. Grant was marching a regiment across Illinois into Missouri and learning how to handle a regiment in the field. He was thirty-nine. He reasoned: "If I were in command of the Northern Army, I'd attack along the Mississippi with a view to cutting Confederate supply lines and army communications." *This reasoning was eventually to win the war.*

Ulysses S. Grant had graduated in 1843 from West Point, fourteen years after Robert E. Lee's graduation from that college. During the Mexican War (1846-1848) Lee had been Ulysses S. Grant's captain.

Susan kept reading the war news with alternate hope and despair. The Union Fleet captured Port Royal, a South Carolina seaport in November 1861. The following March the Confederate *Merrimac* defeated two Union ships near Norfolk Virginia, but next day the Union's *Monitor* forced the

Confederates to retreat. A month later the Union's Admiral Farragut captured New Orleans, and opened to Union forces the southern end of the Mississippi.

Eighteen days before the capture of New Orleans, Susan read of Grant's bloody two-day battle of Shiloh. He had won, and had been made Brigadier-General. A man to watch, Susan told herself. A military genius.

In the summer of 1862, Mr. and Mrs. Stanton and their seven children moved from Seneca Falls to New York City, and Susan went to visit them and help Elizabeth get settled. Now at the age of forty-two, Susan, with her lovely smile, expressive gray eyes, original conversation and alert mind, was an attractive woman. Men were drawn to her and she continued to have opportunities to marry.

Perhaps, as she rocked Elizabeth's youngest child to sleep, Susan may have given thought to all that she had missed by her wholehearted dedication to "the cause," to the exclusion of marriage and motherhood. But no hint of this type of thinking ever found its way into her personal diary, or her journal or letters.

When the Stantons were settled, Susan returned to her father's farm. Daniel Anthony was still working in the Rochester insurance office, and Susan's sister, Mary, was teaching in that city. Each afternoon Daniel and Mary drove home together and sat down to the hot dinner prepared by Susan and her mother. Their evenings were spent in interesting talk of the war and other matters. President Lincoln had just made a proclamation to the effect that all slaves in territory then in rebellion would be freed by the first of January. Daniel and Susan, discussing this Emancipation Proclamation, tried to foresee its consequences.

And then, suddenly, the evening talks with Daniel Anthony came to an end. He had never been sick for a day in his life, but now he began to complain of severe pains near his heart. A doctor ordered him to bed, and on November 25, 1862, at the age of sixty-eight, he died.

Susan felt his death so keenly she could not remain on the farm. She decided that the greatest tribute to this loving father, her best friend, would be to plunge into work for women's rights, and try harder than ever to create for women a world of equality with men. She went to New York City and established Women's Rights Headquarters there.

The Civil War was beginning its third year, and Lincoln's Emancipation Proclamation had freed three million slaves. The Union Army under General Hooker had been badly defeated at Chancellorville, ten miles west of Fredericksburg, but during this battle, "Stonewall" Jackson had been fired upon by mistake by his own men, and died ten days later, on May 10, 1863. Then General Robert E. Lee's army met defeat at Gettysburg, and the very next day General Grant captured Vicksburg, an important town on the Mississippi, thus opening the entire river to Union forces.

As Commander-in-Chief now of the Union Army, General Grant saw to it that Southern ports were blockaded by Union ships and Confederate supply lines were prevented from using the Mississippi. Thus the plan Grant had formulated while colonel of a single regiment only two years before had become today's grim reality.

General Sherman early the next year, began his famous march. He captured Atlanta, remained in that city from May until November, then marched his army toward Savannah, on the sea. During the march of two hundred and twenty-five miles, Georgia's railways, bridges, homes and other buildings, were destroyed.

Susan and Mrs. Stanton, working in New York, longed for peace. It came at last with General Robert E. Lee's surrender to General Grant at Appomattox, Virginia, on April 9, 1865. *But five days later, President Lincoln was assassinated.*

Three hours after President Lincoln's assassination, Vice-President Andrew Johnson took office as the next President. Susan and Elizabeth wondered how he stood on the matter of women's rights. Would he think it fair to give Negro men the vote while withholding it from all women?

This of course is what took place. The Thirteenth Amendment abolished slavery. The Fourteenth Amendment granted voting rights to all *male* citizens.

Susan, although busy with suffrage work, visited her mother as often as possible in Rochester, New York, where Mrs. Anthony had recently bought a two-story brick house. (This house, at 17 Madison Street, is today a National Shrine to Susan's memory.)

And now a rather remarkable event took place. Susan and Mrs. Stanton had happened to meet a wealthy man, George Francis Train. To their surprise he offered to finance for them a weekly newspaper advocating women's rights. They accepted his offer and began publication of the paper, named the *Revolution.* Its motto read: Men, their rights and nothing more. Women, their rights and nothing less. The first copy came out in January, 1868, with Susan as proprietor and Elizabeth Cady Stanton as editor. Even today, copies of the paper make highly interesting reading.

But soon after the launching of the paper, Mr. Train departed for Europe, and although he now and then made contributions to its welfare, almost the entire financial cost fell upon Mrs. Stanton and Susan, who, willing as they were to devote their every waking moment to the project, found newspaper publishing deeply involved in problems and challenges. Susan was forty-eight, Elizabeth fifty-three, when they entered the intricate newspaper world; and they were required to buy huge quantities of paper, hire typesetters and stenographers, pay office rent, obtain subscribers, arrange for newsstand distribution, buy articles from writers, and write whole sections of the paper themselves.

During the two years the paper was published, debts continued to mount. When the *Revolution's* liabilities climbed to ten thousand dollars, Susan sold the paper and she assumed payment of that crushing debt.

She had neither money nor property, but she knew that the public would pay to hear her speak. She joined the Lyceum Circuit, lectured on Woman Suffrage in Eastern towns and cities, and at the end of the year had paid off one thousand dollars.

Now and then, in smaller towns, men attended her talks and acted like bad boys in a classroom. "Go home, old maid!" they'd shout, stamping their feet. They tossed at her rotten eggs and vegetables. One man, after watching Susan's courage in the face of all this, afterward extended an apologetic hand. "I don't believe in women's votes," he told her, "but I *do* believe in *you*, Miss Anthony!"

In January, 1871, Susan and Elizabeth traveled to California, stopping off in Wyoming to congratulate women of that state for winning the right to vote. They lectured in San Francisco, then visited Yosemite Valley where they rode horseback up and down trails until Elizabeth confessed: "I'm pretty nearly jelly. I must stop." Susan, still fresh and vigorous, continued on toward Glacier Point.

On their return to New York, Susan and Elizabeth decided to work for the election to the presidency of General Grant, a Republican. His Democratic opponent, Horace Greeley, had once said to Susan: "As the ballot and the bullet go together, when you vote will you be ready to fight?" She'd answered: "Yes, Mr. Greeley, just as you fought in the last war—at the point of a goose-quill." She had added that never more than ten percent of the male population, in any war, ever sees active combat.

Susan wanted to vote for General Grant. Why not test the Fourteenth Amendment? Why not see whether it gave both men and women citizens the right to cast a ballot?

In Rochester, New York, on November 1, 1872, Susan, her sisters, and several women friends went to the registration office and demanded to be allowed to register. When the man in charge appeared in doubt about the legality of this procedure, Susan read him the Fourteenth Amendment and asked him to point out a single line therein where it discriminated against women. Didn't it say all *persons* born or naturalized in the United States were citizens? Weren't women *persons?* The man agreed that, to the best of his judgment, women surely must be persons. He allowed them to register and thus admitted the name of Susan, her sisters and their friends who had accompanied them that day, to pages of American history.

Susan and the entire group who had registered with her voted on November 5th.

General Grant won the election. Horace Greeley, sorely disappointed, suffered a nervous breakdown and died three weeks later. Susan, who admired him in spite of his refusal to advocate rights for women, wrote that night in her journal: "A giant intellect has suddenly gone out!"

After election, newspapers demanded punishment for the women who had had the effrontery to cast ballots. Susan B. Anthony was arrested and brought to trial in Canandaigua,

New York, before Judge Ward Hunt. She was defended by her good friend, Judge Henry B. Selden.

Sitting straight and attentive in the crowded courtroom, Susan heard Judge Selden defend her right to vote, arguing that his client had taken the only step by which she could bring the constitutional question as to her voting rights before the law of the land. The prosecuting attorney cried: "She has deliberately broken the law and must be punished!"

Judge Hunt told the jury they must bring in a verdict of guilty. And when this verdict was brought in, Judge Hunt made the error of asking Susan if she had anything to say as to why sentence should not be pronounced.

"Yes!" cried Susan, springing to her feet. "Your honor, I have many things to say. My natural rights, my civil rights, my political rights, all have been denied . . ."

The Judge said: "The Court cannot listen to . . ."

"I have been denied the right to testify in my own defense," said Susan. "I have been denied rights never denied in a criminal case except to slaves . . ."

"The prisoner must sit down! She has been tried by due forms of law!"

"Only yesterday, Your Honor, the same man-made forms of law declared it a crime punishable by fine and imprisonment, to give a cup of cold water, a crust of bread, a night's shelter, to a panting fugitive tracking his way to Canada. Yet every man or woman in whose veins courses a drop of human sympathy violated that wicked law, reckless of consequences, and was justified in doing so. And then . . ."

"The Court must insist . . ."

"And then, Your Honor, the slaves had to take it over, under or through the unjust forms of law, precisely as now women must take it, to get a voice in this government. And I mean to take it at every opportunity!"

"Will you sit down!"

"Failing to get this justice, Your Honor, I ask not leniency at your hands, but rather the full rigor of the law."

The Judge drew a long breath. "I fine you one hundred dollars and full costs of the prosecution."

"I shall never pay a dollar of your unjust penalty," said Susan.

The Judge dismissed the Court.

And so ended one of America's famous trials, involving the rights of half the population. Susan did not pay the fine. None of the women who had voted with her were brought to justice. But because she had not received a fair trial, sympathy was with her throughout the land in daily conversations and in newspapers.

Now her audiences grew larger, and she began to make more money to pay the debt she owed on the *Revolution*, her recent newspaper. Anson Lapham, her cousin, who had lent her four thousand dollars for the paper's expenses, suddenly canceled her debt to him. And in 1876, six years after she had assumed payment of the ten thousand dollars, she paid the last dollar of it and was free.

Newspapers throughout the country praised her. "She has paid her debts like a man," wrote one editor. "Not so! Not one man in a thousand but would have settled at ten cents on the dollar."

Susan continued her speaking tour, growing accustomed to "living in a suitcase." She wore black silk dresses, for they could be sponged and pressed each evening after a lecture; her hostess usually offering sponge and iron at Susan's request.

The work was tiring, but Susan's excellent health sustained her. After a day of travel, then dinner, then a lecture, then talk with host and hostess, sleep came to Susan swiftly, no matter how scanty the bedclothing or lumpy the mattress.

She now earned forty dollars a lecture and could afford a hotel room. But she preferred to stay in private homes because it gave her opportunity to convert members of the family to women's rights.

Such was the spell of her voice, the quiet logic of her words, that she seldom failed to win friends in every home. Long after children in various homes where she'd stayed were grown up, they would speak of "the night when Miss Anthony stayed at our house," and go on to tell their listeners why women should be allowed to cast a ballot.

Susan was now in her sixties. Her slim figure's erect carriage, her animated talk, infectious laughter, kept the years from showing.

In 1880, Susan's mother died, leaving the Rochester home to Susan's sister, Mary. The mother, before her death, confided to a friend: "If I leave the home to Susan, she'd sell it and give the money to the cause of Women's Rights."

That same year, Susan and Elizabeth began to work on a History of Woman Suffrage, and two years later they'd completed two volumes, each one thousand pages long! Then Mrs. Stanton sailed for Europe.

Elizabeth began to deluge Susan with letters from Europe. Why not come to see the wonderful city of London? Susan finally decided to go. Six days after her sixty-third birthday, she sailed for Liverpool on the *British Prince*, sat at the Captain's table, and completely converted him to women's rights.

Elizabeth met the ship when it docked, and for a week the two friends toured London town. At the Tower of London, Susan stood beside the block upon which 17-year-old Jane Gray had been beheaded, for *being* Lady Jane Gray. "The poor child," said Susan, tears in her eyes. "I hope she's forgiven us."

They walked through Chelsea's narrow streets, imagining
Sir Thomas More, Joseph Addison, Jonathan Swift, walking
there. As Jonathan Swift had done in Chelsea a hundred years
before, they bought a Chelsea bun. Swift had "paid a penny
for it and pronounced it stale." Elizabeth eating her bun without enthusiasm, laughed and said: "I pronounce this stale,
too."

Just off Fleet Street they lunched in the restaurant fre-
quented the century before, by Samuel Johnson.

"Do you remember Johnson's advice to a young man who
had asked him whether or not to marry a girl of high intelligence?"

Elizabeth could not remember Johnson's advice. What was
it?

"Well," said Susan, "the young man was worried for fear
the girl might outshine him."

"And what did Johnson say?"

"He told the young man to go ahead and marry the girl.
Johnson assured the young man that before a year was out,
he'd find the girl's reason weaker and her wit not so bright."

Elizabeth stared at the empty chair with Johnson's name
engraved on it. The great man had sat here. But she kept to
herself her opinion of his dire prophecy concerning wives.
This restaurant, where he'd enjoyed so many good meals did
not seem the proper place for her to hold forth upon women's
rights.

After a week of sight-seeing, the two friends parted. Susan
went to Italy to view Rome's fabulous statuary, historic
ruins, the Colosseum by moonlight. In Naples she marveled
at the shoreline's unparalleled beauty, and strolled in painful
disillusionment through Naples' streets of desperate slums.

She toured Germany, Switzerland, France. Then she returned to the British Isles. During this first vacation of her

life, she awoke each morning to a strange, new, enjoyable world without work.

In Scotland she climbed to the top floor of a palace, up hundreds of stairs, and in a small room was allowed a glimpse into a mirror *supposedly* owned by Mary, Queen of Scots. She was driven by a park wherein stood a bathhouse Mary, Queen of Scots, had used; and she ate strawberries from a garden that had supplied them to the lovely queen 300 years before. Indeed, Susan's stout and ample shoes kept matching imprints made by Mary, Queen of Scots' immortal feet.

As Susan stood on the bank of Loch Lomond, she wanted to say aloud that this lake was no more beautiful than are several of New York State's Finger Lakes. But she kept politely silent. That night, however, she wrote to her sister, Mary: "There is nothing more beautiful here than we have in America, only everything here has more historic and poetic association."

She returned to London to address Suffrage meetings planned in her honor; and with Elizabeth Cady Stanton she launched an International Suffrage Organization. She went shopping and bought an India shawl. (This shawl may today be seen in Rochester's Municipal Museum.)

In November, 1883, Susan and Elizabeth returned to the United States, and Susan made her headquarters at Riggs House in Washington, D.C. The hotel was owned by one of Susan's friends and a room was provided for her always without charge.

She visited Congress and pleaded with Congressmen to support a Federal Amendment giving women the right to vote. They promised to help with this, but she knew from past experience the vast chasm between promises and action. At year's end Congress adjourned without passing the Amendment, but Susan had learned to look failure in the face, time

and again, without really seeing it. "Failure," she told Elizabeth Cady Stanton, "is only an incomplete job."

About this time, one of Susan's friends died and left Susan
a legacy of several thousand dollars, to be used for the cause
of Women's Rights. Susan and Elizabeth began work on
volume III of the History of Woman Suffrage, knowing that
they'd now have the money with which to publish it.

In March, 1888, the International Suffrage Organization
held a meeting in Washington, D. C., and a young woman
minister, Dr. Anna Shaw, spoke before it. This was the beginning of Susan's friendship with Dr. Shaw. Two years later she
acquired another friend of Suffrage; Carrie Chapman Catt.

Now Susan began to wear spectacles, her hair was turning
white, but she still walked very straight and wore, quite
regally, a red shawl that had been given her by a friend. The
shawl became so well known in Washington that an editor of
that city wrote: "The seasons in Washington are not heralded
by the appearance of the first robin in spring, nor the first
snowflakes in winter, but by the coming and going of Miss
Anthony in her red shawl."

In 1891, Susan decided to go to live with her sister, Mary,
in Rochester. Shortly after she made this decision, the Rochester Equality League surprised her by refurnishing the
house to make it look as nearly as possible like the home she
remembered in her mother's day. The League searched
throughout the state for bed, tables, chairs, the old desk Susan
had used, and the many other pieces of furniture that had
been in the Anthony family. Susan, walking from room to
room, felt her heart warm with loving memories. *This was
home.*

She spent the summer of 1893 at the World's Fair in Chicago, and when she spoke before the women's organizations
gathered there, vast audiences applauded her and cheered.

As she walked through the Fair grounds, crowds followed her, eager for a glimpse of the famous Susan B. Anthony.

During her very active seventies, she spoke in cities of every state from Maine to California. And in California, Mrs. Phoebe Hearst personally handed her one thousand dollars for the Suffrage cause.

She took another trip to England and made many speeches there, then came home to write "The Life and Work of Susan B. Anthony," in three volumes, with the aid of a former newspaper woman, Mrs. Ida Husted Harper. She finished the fourth volume of "History of Woman Suffrage," and then took time out from her suffrage work to raise one hundred thousand dollars demanded by Rochester University before that institution of higher learning would admit girls. Susan borrowed on her life insurance policy for this project, when her friends had given, at personal sacrifice, as much as possible. And at last she was able to write in her diary: "Well, Rochester University let the girls in."

On October 26, 1902, Elizabeth Cady Stanton died, leaving Susan with a deep sense of bereavement. She wrote many articles for magazines and newspapers, telling about her beloved friend's many contributions to the public good.

During her eighties, Susan traveled to Berlin, and was entertained by Germany's Empress, Augusta Victoria; and then she journeyed to England to meet the young and beautiful Emmeline Pankhurst, who would later become famous.

At the age of eighty-five, Susan admitted she felt "a little tired" now and then. In a letter to a friend, she wrote: "Oh, to be sixty-five again!"

On her eighty-sixth birthday, against her doctor's advice, she went to Washington D. C. to attend a dinner in her honor. In her speech there she praised men who had helped her, men who believed whole-heartedly in women's rights.

"To desire liberty for oneself is a natural instinct," she said. "But to be willing to accord liberty to another is the result of education, self-discipline, and the practice of the Golden Rule."

Less than a month after she'd made this speech, Susan B. Anthony died on March 6, 1906. Flags throughout the country flew at half mast.

One hundred years after her birth, fourteen years after her death, the nineteenth Amendment was written into our Constitution and all women citizens of the United States were granted the right to vote. Since then, women have accepted this as an inalienable right.

Although Susan B. Anthony knew neither marriage nor motherhood, it might be said she mothered the new woman. In hearts and minds of India's women lawyers, Burma's women scientists, America's women who stay in the home or march each morning to well-paid jobs, her spirit lives. It will live in dreams and contributions of women yet unborn. *These are her daughters.*

5

MARY BAKER EDDY

(1821-1910)

On a Sunday morning in 1839, Mary Baker, eighteen, was teaching Infants' Class in the Congregational Church Sunday School in Tilton, New Hampshire. She was slim and of medium height, with curling chestnut hair, and her very blue eyes changed in color to deep violet as she earnestly explained the Bible verses to a half dozen little girls seated in a semi-circle about her chair.

The children, responding to her love for them, did their best to memorize the text. They liked the simple good lines of her dress, and her clear pleasant voice. And although they did not realize it, here was a teacher they'd remember all their lives.

When the lesson was over, mothers came for their children, and Mary remained in the empty classroom to place small chairs in a neat row. Neatness was second nature to her. Then she put on her coat and pretty straw bonnet, and went out and down the church steps. To her surprise, there stood her favorite brother, Albert.

He smiled. "May I walk you home?"

She laughed and fell into step beside him. Albert, eleven

years her senior, was a practising lawyer in Hillsborough, New Hampshire, and had been elected to the New Hampshire State Legislature. She did not ask when he'd arrived or how long he could stay. Instead, she concentrated on the joy of having him to herself during the short walk, at least.

On the road to the Baker farm they passed friends who stopped to talk for a moment and Albert's eyes lighted at their interest in his career. Mary glanced up at him with pride. He was well built and tall, with wavy dark auburn hair. Five years ago, on graduation from Dartmouth, he'd won a Phi Beta Kappa key.

Toward the edge of town they met fewer people and could talk without interruption. They spoke of his summer holidays while attending Dartmouth. He'd spent them on the Baker farm and had tutored Mary.

"Wonderful, Albert, that you'd want to share with me some of your Dartmouth learning!"

He smiled. "*You* should talk of sharing. Remember how, as a child, you'd give away your toys? And at school you'd give your mittens to a little girl who had none? Once you came home without your warm winter coat."

They laughed and he put a hand under her arm to guide her around a bad place in the road.

"You always liked to write poetry, Mary. And you talked of someday writing a book. You've started it?"

"Not yet. Perhaps I shall."

"If you don't get married."

She looked up into his face. "Should marriage put an end to the writing of books?"

"No." He grew immediately serious. "Of course not. I didn't mean that it should."

They'd now reached higher ground and in the distance could see the Baker farmhouse. It was not the one where

Mary, her two older sisters and three older brothers were born. That had been at Bow, New Hampshire. Four years ago, in January, 1835, Grandmother Baker had died; and in January, 1836, Mark Baker, Mary's father, had moved his family here. This house, built on a rise, had a background of blue mountains.

Albert stood a moment looking at the farmhouse. "Home!" he said. "I can see inside as plainly as if we'd already entered it. Big parlor with its air of warm hospitality. Great dining table with the old Bible on the nearby stand."

Mary nodded. "Inside the Bible, the names of our ancestors, with John Baker of 1634 heading the list."

Albert smiled. "Yes, husky old John Baker, who sailed from England, landed in Massachusetts, cleared the wilderness, built a home. A pioneer." He looked down at his sister. "Mary, you and I must become pioneers, too. In our own way."

They walked on thoughtfully toward the house.

Yes, Mary told herself, someday she'd write a book. And become, in her own way, a pioneer.

It all came true. She was indeed to write a book. And in spite of her delicate appearance and slight build, John Baker's great-great-great-great-great-granddaughter would live to become a pioneer. She'd perform the hardy task of clearing a path through traditional thought and building a new religion.

During the four years following this conversation with Albert, Mary Baker continued to live with her parents in the Tilton farmhouse. She read the Bible daily, helped her mother with the housework, attended school at times, and tried to please her hard working father, who was not only deeply religious but a very strict disciplinarian.

Before Mary's twenty-second birthday her cousin, Dr.

Alpheus B. Morrill, came to Tilton to practice a new type of medicine; homeopathy. At first Mark Baker was skeptical of Dr. Morrill's little white pills, but after he'd heard reports of cures, he decided Dr. Morrill should treat Mary, who was troubled with pains in her back.

Mary showed improvement under the doctor's administrations of white pills and became interested in homeopathy. This interest would play a part in her future career.

On October 21, 1841, her beloved brother Albert died, at the age of thirty-two, after a short illness. He had been nominated to Congress, and was on the threshold of an inspiring future. His political antagonist, the Honorable Isaac Hill, of Concord, wrote "Albert Baker was a young man of uncommon promise. Gifted with the highest order of intellectual powers, he trained and schooled them by intense and almost incessant study throughout his short life."

Mary, as a child of ten and a guest at her brother Sam's marriage to Eliza Glover of Concord, met for the first time the bride's brother: George Washington Glover, dark-eyed, handsome, intelligent, and twenty-one. Five years later, at her sister Abigail's wedding, Mary encountered this young man. Seven years went by, and now Mary, age twenty-two, attending the wedding of her sister, Martha, once more met George Washington Glover as a wedding guest. By this time he saw Mary as a lovely and desirable young woman, and in her eyes he'd become a Prince Charming. They fell deeply in love.

On December 10, 1843, young Mary Baker and George Washington Glover were married in the parlor of the Baker farmhouse, the ceremony being attended by Mary's parents, her brothers Samuel and George, with their wives; her sisters Abigail Tilton and Martha Pilsbury with their husbands, and many friends who came in sleighs from town, or from nearby farms. Dr. Enoch Corser, pastor of the Baker family, officiated.

Their wedding night was spent at Concord, and they drove next day to Bow, Mary's birthplace. From there they went to Boston and took a ship for Charleston, South Carolina, where George Glover had a prosperous contracting business. They arrived in Charleston shortly before Christmas.

Mary's mother, left at home in Tilton, sorely missed her youngest child. She wrote to her: "Mary, dear child, everything reminds me of you. Sometimes I fear I worship Mary instead of the great Jehovah. . . ."

Mary missed her mother; but her new home and young husband, the great adventure of marriage, filled her heart with happiness. George Glover, a freemason, had a wide circle of friends and acquaintances in Charleston, and all extended kindness and hospitality to his bride.

It is interesting to speculate upon what might have happened to countless Christian Science churches all over the world if George Glover had lived through middle and old age and Mary had found fulfillment in the role of wife and mother, in the management of a well-ordered home. What of those churches and the army of men and women who today attend them? But of course "if" is too large a word, one too fraught with dangerous magic, to be tossed about by human curiosity.

In February of 1844, Mary traveled with her husband on a business trip to Wilmington, North Carolina, and there he caught yellow fever. George Glover was sick for nine days and on his deathbed, with his parting breath, gave directions to his brother Masons about accompanying Mary to her home in New Hampshire.

After his death, Mary remained for a month in the South,

then a Mr. Cooke, a Mason, accompanied her to New York where she was met by her brother, George Sullivan Baker. She was still only twenty-two, now a widow, and would become a mother in September.

In the Tilton farmhouse, Mary's parents gave her tender care, but she found it difficult to adjust to the loss of her young husband. By her twenty-third birthday, July 16, 1844, she may have recovered a small degree of light heartedness, for she decided to "count her mercies" and be grateful for present blessings rather than grieve for trials past. She wrote this philosophy into a short poem.

Mary's son was born on September 12, 1844 and named George Washington Glover, after his father. She did not regain strength enough to undertake the baby's care, and her father gave the child to a Mrs. Amos Morrison to nurse. Later the baby was brought home, and Mary once more tried to care for him, but was not well enough to do so.

Mahala Sanborn, the local blacksmith's daughter, had been engaged as Mary's nurse, and at night she would take the baby home with her. This arrangement went on for some time, but when Mary still found herself not physically vigorous enough to care for her dearly loved little boy, Mahala Sanborn was permitted to keep him.

Mary's husband had been a successful builder, and it was reasonable to suppose she might receive money from his estate. But in those days communication between Tilton and Charleston was difficult. Lumber owned by Mary's husband had been piled upon Wilmington's wharf, and was lost. In the final settlement of her husband's affairs, Mary received not a penny.

She continued to live at home, and began to write stories, poems, even a novelette. Thus was she displaying evidence of writing talent years before her discovery of Christian Science.

About this time Mark Baker moved his family into the new home he'd built next door to Abigail's house in Tilton. Mrs. Baker became ill when she'd lived in the new home about a year and after six months of illness she died. She had been dead only a year when Mark Baker married a Mrs. Elizabeth Patterson Duncan. Mary moved in with her sister, Abigail.

It was after the death of Mary's mother that Mahala Sanborn decided to marry Russell Cheney of Groton, N. H., and Mahala asked permission to take little George Glover with her to Groton. Mary reluctantly consented.

There is no record of Mary's attendance at any spiritualist meeting, though spiritualism, mesmerism, and animal magnetism were now widely discussed throughout New England. Mary, years later, wrote of spiritualism: "When the Science of Mind is understood, spiritualism will be found mainly erroneous, having no scientific basis nor origin, no proof nor power outside of human testimony."

But it is interesting to note that Franz Anton Mesmer, born in Austria in 1734, had evolved a new theory of the power of mental suggestion, and, as a disowned offshoot of his teachings, spiritualism was born. Mesmer first studied to be a priest, then studied law, then at the age of thirty-one took his Doctor of Medicine degree in Vienna. He mentioned in his college thesis the word *fluidum*, describing it as an invisible ether-like substance flowing through the nervous system, affecting the muscles, and *by some magic curing sickness*. He termed this fluidum: *animal magnetism*.

Although Mesmer could not explain animal magnetism cures, he denied that they were in any sense religious. And although he had graduated with honors from Medical College, then spent his first five years after graduation in private practice, administering medicine to patients as prescribed by Medical School teaching, he kept thinking of fluidum's unexplained curative qualities.

He decided to try fluidum, or animal magnetism, upon patients; and to his astonishment was successful in effecting many cures. As his fame spread, and his fluidum cures became numerous, Vienna doctors grew unsympathetic and forced Mesmer to leave the city. He practiced in Paris until a Commission of Inquiry questioned his healings and practically forced him into retirement.

After Mesmer's death in 1814, students of "mesmerism" carried his teaching down strange new paths, inventing terms such as "auto-suggestion," "hypnosis," "spiritualism." Eventually these terms appeared in conversations of citizens of Tilton, New Hampshire.

In 1852 Mary Baker Glover grew interested in her stepmother's nephew, Dr. Daniel Patterson, a dentist. She'd met him in her father's home, and he was big, handsome, with a hearty laugh, and with every appearance of possessing strength of character. She saw him as a desirable companion, as a wise step-father for little George. They were married on June 21, 1853.

He was kind to Mary, and they lived peaceably up to the time of the divorce, but he refused to make a home for Mary's young son. In 1856 Mahala and Russell Cheney moved to Minnesota and took twelve-year-old George Glover with them, leaving Mary to wonder unhappily when, if ever, she would see the boy again.

Mary had been in ill health for years, and doctors termed her trouble a "spinal affliction." She was forced to employ someone to help with the housework, and to care for her, and for these duties she chose a blind girl, Myra Smith.

In 1861 Dr. Patterson's concern for his wife's ill health became an important factor in Mary's future career. On the 14th of October of that year, Dr. Patterson wrote to a Dr. Pineas Parkhurst Quimby, a magnetic healer in Portland, Maine, of whom he'd heard remarkable stories of magic cures. He asked Dr. Quimby to treat Mary either in Portland, or in Concord. Dr. Quimby replied he had no doubt he could cure her if she'd come to his Portland office, and he enclosed with his reply a circular containing his philosophy. Dr. Patterson handed the reply and the circular to Mary.

The Civil War had begun in April of 1861, and early in 1862 Dr. Patterson was commissioned to go to Washington to collect a fund for Southerners who sympathized with the Union. He had hoped to secure an appointment on the army medical staff, but never did, and in March, 1862, was captured by the South and sent to Libby Prison.

On October 10, 1862, Mary arrived in Portland by boat, and went to Dr. Quimby's office. She was helped up the stairs by Dr. Quimby's son, as she felt too weak to climb them unaided.

Dr. Quimby, a kindly man of sixty, with deep-set dark eyes, luxuriant white hair and a white beard, received her sympathetically. He said: "Whatever we believe, that we create. Your pain is caused by fear, and fear comes from belief in disease. Man is in bondage to human beliefs."

While Mary sat in a chair, he began to gently manipulate her head. "Get rid of the image of sickness," he said. "Establish in its place the truth, or health."

Mary, accepting his words, and reading into them a deep

spiritual meaning that perhaps he did not intend, stood up and walked without pain. She left the office, apparently cured.

But she remained in Portland and had frequent talks with Dr. Quimby. At the end of the week she climbed one hundred and eighty steps to the dome of the City Hall, for a view of the city.

After returning home she corresponded with Dr. Quimby, and learned the salient facts of his career. He, like Franz Anton Mesmer, was a mesmerist, and could not explain his cures.

In 1865 Mary and Dr. Patterson took rooms in the fishing village of Swampscott, near Lynn, Massachusetts. He had escaped from the military prison, and had come home to find her in good health. That year Mark Baker, Mary's father, died, but he left Mary no share of his property.

On January 16, 1866, Dr. Quimby died. And even though his philosophy had not held all the answers she sought, Mary realized his greatness as a man and a humanitarian.

Just two weeks after Dr. Quimby's death, on the first of February, Mary had an experience that not only changed her entire life but would change the lives of countless human beings yet unborn.

She was on her way to a Temperance meeting in Lynn, about a mile from Swampscott, walking with friends. On this cold night the pavements were icy. Near the corner of Oxford and Market Streets in Lynn, she slipped on the ice and fell, injuring her spine. Friends carried Mary, unconscious, into a nearby house, and Dr. Alvin M. Cushing was called. He came, examined her, found her injuries to be critical, and expressed a fear that she would never walk again.

Next morning, which was Friday, she was wrapped warmly in furs and driven in a sleigh to her home in Swampscott and put to bed. She was suffering intense pain, with muscle spasms, and when the doctor was again called he could do little to help.

By Sunday morning her condition was unchanged and she lay in bed, suffering greatly, unable to move her legs. Neighbors, watching at her bedside spoke in whispers; and one of them, thinking Mary was dying, sent for a minister.

Mary suddenly asked for her Bible, and when it was brought to her she requested that she might be left alone. The neighbors reluctantly withdrew and closed the bedroom door.

Mary opened her Bible to the ninth chapter of Matthew and began to read about the man sick of the palsy to whom Jesus said, "Arise!"

And now, as if a candle had been lighted in her consciousness, Mary saw the miracle's explanation. The sick man, helpless, disillusioned, hopeless, had turned to the arms of Divine Love. The love of Christ Jesus flowed in unbroken harmony to the sick man, *and it was Jesus' understanding that God had already made the man perfect, whole, that brought about the man's healing.*

Mary, glimpsing the fact that the only reality of existence is *Life in and of the Spirit,* seemed to hear the Master say to her: "Arise." She arose from her bed, instantly healed. She found her clothes and dressed. Presently someone knocked on the door and a concerned voice said:

"The minister is here."

Mary, smiling, walked to the door and opened it.

During the months that followed, Mary tried by ceaseless study of the Bible and earnest prayer to put what she had discovered into exact and scientific words that would state the *Law of Healing*. This law would bestow upon humanity the gift of mental and physical health.

She was aware that for two hundred years after the death of Christ Jesus, devout Christians had employed the divine law of healing to effect many cures. Then the law of healing had been lost. Now that she had rediscovered it and regained her own health thereby, she could not rest until she'd framed the principle in direct words of a mathematical formula.

The healing of the palsied man had been in no sense a blind faith cure. His healing had been due to Christ Jesus' *understanding* that God had already made the man perfect, whole.

She grew convinced that we are Soul, not body. She used the word Soul as a synonym for God, not for man; and only in his true spiritual nature was man the expression or reflection of Soul. She was one day to write: "When man is spoken of as made in God's image, it is not sinful and sickly mortal man who is referred to, but the ideal man, reflecting God's image."

Mary reasoned that her own prayers had failed to heal her in early years because she'd not then discerned the spiritual sense of the creed in the Science of Christianity. She understood now that "It is the living, palpitating presence of Christ, Truth, which heals the sick."

One day Mary's Bible study was interrupted by news that Dr. Patterson, her husband, had "eloped" with a neighbor's wife. This was in the summer of 1866, six months after Mary's fall on the ice. The news shocked and disturbed her, but Mary determined to demonstrate her newly discovered key to mental health by handling the situation in the manner she had handled her recent physical pain.

She learned that the neighbor's wife now regretted running away with Dr. Patterson and tried to return to her husband. But the husband refused forgiveness.

The distressed wife then came to Mary and begged her to talk with the wronged husband and try to persuade him to give her another chance. After an earnest conversation with the neighbor, Mary convinced him that his erring wife was truly sorry, and he allowed her to return.

Dr. Patterson came to Mary and asked her forgiveness, but she would not consent to live with him again. He offered her two hundred dollars a year for her support during their permanent separation, and this she accepted.

Two hundred dollars a year, less than seventeen dollars a month, was very little income, even in 1866, but Mary made the best of it. She boarded in a Lynn family's home, and spent her days studying and writing, allowing herself no outside social life. She conversed with the family at meal-times, and tried to explain the healing truths she'd recently learned.

Now she was forty-five, slender, graceful and attractive, with brilliant blue eyes that held a listener's attention while she talked. She wore her brown hair parted in the middle and in curls, according to a hair style of that day.

During the next three years she moved frequently. Moving was a simple process, for she had only to fill her one suit-case with manuscripts, writing materials, her Bible, and her few articles of clothing.

At the outset of these three years of intense Bible study, she began healing, and her first patient was Dorr Phillips, a boy attending school. His Quaker parents lived in Lynn, and were Mary's devoted friends, Dorr's father being the first to listen intelligently to Mary's discussion of the new mental state that was later to be termed Christian Science.

Dorr had a bone felon that was extremely painful, and

Mary asked if he would let her heal it. He said yes. Mary then asked him to promise not to do anything for it, or let anyone else do anything for it, if she undertook its cure. He promised. That evening, when asked about his finger, he said it didn't hurt. He actually forgot about it, and when he did think of it again, the finger was well.

Next she healed a young man of fever; and later she healed a Mrs. Abbie Winslow who had not walked for years. Mary took no personal credit for these cures, but said that God would do the healing if the patient would let Him.

It was still 1866, and in the house where Mary boarded were a Mr. and Mrs. Hiram S. Crafts. Mr. Crafts, seated beside Mary at table, grew interested in her talk of Mind Healing; and when he and his wife moved from Lynn to Stoughton, Massachusetts, Mary went with them and lived in their home. She began to write out her ideas in manuscript form, and from this manuscript, also from the Scriptures, began to teach Hiram S. Crafts, her first pupil.

Mr. and Mrs. Crafts moved to the neighboring town of Taunton, and again Mary went with them. Mr. Crafts opened an office here and advertised for patients. He was able to cure a woman patient of an internal abscess from which she'd suffered for twelve years, and at this healing the patient and her friends expressed great astonishment. Mary, who continued to teach Mr. Crafts during the evening, now saw that she not only could demonstrate religious healing herself, but *she could teach others to demonstrate it.*

Mary now moved to Amesbury, Massachusetts, and boarded with a Mrs. Nathaniel Webster. Every waking moment of each day and evening Mary continued to search her Bible for a better understanding of God's power to heal sickness, and she strove for clearness of expression as she put this healing science into words. Later, she wrote: "The search was sweet, calm, and buoyant with hope, not selfish nor depressing."

In the late summer of 1868 Mary moved to the home of Miss Sarah Bagley, to whom she taught the doctrine of Christian Science. Later Miss Bagley practiced the art of healing, but did not strictly follow Mary's teaching, as she confused it with mesmerism.

Mary began to instruct students individually, writing down for them the important points in her lessons. She also gave talks to groups of people assembled in parlors of various homes. Now and then she wrote a poem, and several are used as hymns today in Christian Science churches.

In the Spring of 1870, Mary returned to the city of Lynn accompanied by young Richard Kennedy whom she had instructed, and who wanted to practice Mind Science. He urged her to allow him to practice healing in partnership with her, and she consented.

They rented rooms in a house facing the Lynn Common, and Mary was to receive half of any income he received from his healing. This arrangement went on for two years and then they dissolved partnership because of divergence of views, as Kennedy practiced mesmerism.

Until 1870, lack of money had given Mary much concern. But she suddenly realized that the matter of *supply* could and should be handled exactly as one handled matters of health. Her money need, as well as all her needs, was already met, wasn't it, by the generous abundance of God? Yes! From that day on, *her fear of lack of money entirely vanished*.

She decided she should not teach her students free of charge, for no one truly appreciates what he does not pay for. Beginning in 1870, she charged one hundred dollars for ten class lessons.

The writing of her book, which Mary decided to call

Science and Health was going well, and she at last received money from teaching and healing. Before long she had a bank account of a few thousand dollars.

Mary said God had "dictated" *Science and Health*, and her pen had merely transcribed His dictation. As proof, she admitted she found it necessary to study certain passages of *Science and Health* before she could understand them.

She used terms in the book that are now familiar language of her religion. She spelled Mind with a capital letter when used to mean God; and the other mind—mortal mind as she called it—she spelled with a small letter. The corporeal body she termed *matter*.

She classified sin, disease, death and matter as errors of mortal mind, and taught that the material body is an expression of the conscious and unconscious thoughts of mortals. Hence she firmly believed that *replacing the errors of mortal mind with the truth of immortal Mind brings healing to the body*.

In 1873, seven years after their permanent separation, Mary applied for and obtained a divorce from Dr. Patterson on the ground of desertion. Two years later she bought her first home, a two-story frame house, with an attic, at Number 8 Broad Street in Lynn.

Mary was now in excellent health and seldom tired, even after writing all day and teaching evening classes, and practising healing in her spare time. Her fame as a healer was spreading.

During her healings, she first swept her mind of fear, then declared the truth. By "declaring the truth" she meant she saw the patient already perfect and whole, a reflection of God's image. She expected a complete cure.

Once Mary described her healing work to a student in

the following words: "I saw the love of God encircling the universe and man, filling all space, and that divine Love so permeated my own consciousness that I loved with Christlike compassion everything I saw."

On Sunday morning, June 6, 1875, Mary preached a sermon in Good Templars' Hall. Eight students had made arrangements for this series to begin, and of course many more students attended. They all sang hymns. That day the eight students pledged, together, ten dollars a week to hire a hall for future Sunday services.

In October of that year the first edition of Science and Health—one thousand copies—was published. Critics wrote of it: *"This book is indeed wholly original, but it will never be read."*

A very important event took place in Mary's life the next Spring. A young man came down from Boston to take treatment from Mary for an illness. He was cured, and joined Mary's class for instruction. The young man, forty-four at the time, was of medium height and handsome, with a keen sense of humor and a smile that put one's world at peace. His alert mind eagerly absorbed Mary's teaching, and on graduation from her classes he opened his own office and was the first of her students to announce himself publicly: *Christian Scientist*. He inscribed these two words upon a sign and below them his name: Asa Gilbert Eddy.

Asa Gilbert Eddy's ancestors came to America in 1630, and among his forbears were governors and ministers. He himself had owned a large New England farm, but had lately earned his living as a salesman. Asa Gilbert Eddy possessed a kind heart, tremendous industry, and was to some extent gifted in both art and music. One of his important and unusual accomplishments was the ability to go into a kitchen and concoct a delicious meal. His gentleness, spirituality, success in Mind Healing, won Mary's heart. They were married on New Year's Day, 1877.

It was characteristic of Asa Gilbert Eddy that he recognized no age difference between Mary and himself. She was fifty-six when they were married, but to him, looking at her through the eyes of love, she appeared to be only forty. That was the age he recorded for her on their marriage license; and years later, when she discovered his error, Mary could not repress a tender smile.

She often said that a good marriage was a union of the affections that tended to lift mortals higher. This described her marriage to Asa Gilbert Eddy. At every turn, she relied upon his help; and he gave of himself with such complete devotion, such cheerful good nature, that daily he grew more dear to her. He, in turn, loved her deeply. He said of Mary: " 'My wife is the most unselfish individual I have ever known, and the most tireless in her duty.' "

Partners in such a marriage could not but prosper, and the next five years saw them building firm foundations beneath Mary's career. Between 1876 and 1882 so much was accomplished that a list of achievements leaves one breathless with amazement.

During these years Mary alone was responsible for founding the Christian Scientist Association, the Church of Christ, Scientist, and the Massachusetts Metaphysical College. Asa Gilbert Eddy published the second and third editions of Science and Health, and made a study of copyright laws. They both taught classes, and they both healed many people who came with personal problems, or with mental or physical illness.

The third edition of *Science and Health* contains the now

familiar "scientific statement of being," and also THE CROSS AND THE CROWN, a symbol of the power of Truth over crosses met in daily living.

Mary had preached her science of healing from pulpits of various Boston churches since 1878, and thought perhaps these churches might accept her teachings as part of their own. She discovered, however, that congregations of these churches were not ready to accept Christian Science. She realized she must have a church of her own.

She obtained a charter for the Church of Christ, Scientist, in 1879, and two years later a charter to open in Boston the Massachusetts Metaphysical College, wherein students were instructed in Christian Science principles, and where Mary could confer degrees. Mary taught all the Primary and Normal classes, with very few exceptions.

In 1879, she received word that her son, George Washington Glover, now married and the father of a family, was living in the Northwest. She immediately wired him an invitation to come to see her, and he accepted. Their dramatic meeting affected her deeply, but she found her son to be a stranger to her way of thinking. Still, she loved him and gave him her blessing. He stayed several weeks, then left for home.

Two years later she was surprised by a revolt among her students. Eight of them withdrew from her church. Mary managed to rise above this distressing experience, and preserved her existing church organization. Among her loyal followers was a student named Calvin Frye, and on a future day when she needed a reliable helper, she was to remember him.

Mr. Eddy suggested that they go to Washington, D.C. where he might make a more thorough study of copyright laws with a view to the legal protection of Mary's writings. Mary went with him, and the study required several months. Ever afterward she was grateful for her husband's painstaking investigation of this important phase of her work.

They returned to Boston from Washington in April, 1882, and Mary plunged into long hours of work each day, preaching, teaching, healing. Many were her conferences with students of the Massachusetts Metaphysical College, and many were the problems brought to her, and to Mr. Eddy.

Suddenly, in the midst of all these activities, Mr. Eddy's health began to fail. Mary offered to treat him, but he told her he wished to treat himself, and felt confident he could do this. On June 2nd he was well enough to go for a drive, but on June 3rd, just before daybreak, he died of a heart attack.

The shock of her husband's death, after five years and five months of marriage, was so deep that Mary left Boston for the Vermont hills and spent the summer there. Mary wrote a few weeks later to a friend: "I can't yet feel much interest in anything on earth. I shall try and eventually succeed in rising from the gloom of my irreparable loss but it must take *time*."

In the same letter she wrote that she would never forget dear, dear Gilbert whose memory was "dearer every day." She added that the hills and vales and lakes of Vermont were lovely but "this was his native state and *he is not here*."

Toward the end of the summer, Mary began to consider the qualifications of various students with a view to selecting one who could look after her household and protect her time and energies from unnecessary interruptions. She thought of Calvin A. Frye of Lawrence, Massachusetts, and sent him a telegram.

Mr. Frye, who had been practicing Christian Science in Lawrence, came at once in response to Mary's telegram and met her at Plymouth, New Hampshire, as she was returning to Boston. On the train between Plymouth and Boston, she questioned him and discovered him to be sincerely eager to serve the cause of Christian Science in any capacity. She remembered that Mr. Eddy had recommended Mr. Frye as a man to be trusted.

Calvin Frye was thirty-seven when he responded to her wire that August day in 1882. His wife had died ten years before, just a year after their marriage. His father, a Harvard man, had been a classmate of Ralph Waldo Emerson; and Frye's fine old New England family was of pioneer stock. Calvin Frye himself, of medium height and stout, had a gentle nature and a keen sense of humor. He knew bookkeeping and shorthand, was strictly honest, and for the next twenty-eight years, to the end of Mary's life on earth, he held the position of private secretary to the founder of Christian Science.

What Mary accomplished during the last quarter century of her life seems almost miraculous. She was sixty-one years of age when Gilbert Eddy died in 1882; and it has been said, though probably not with truth, that if she'd died at sixty, the world would never have recorded her name. It is certain that her work *after* sixty brought Christian Science to full fruitage and made it a power in the land.

On April 14, 1883, she published the first issue of a bi-monthly magazine containing messages to her followers and a list of reliable Christian Science practitioners. Today this is a monthly periodical, the Christian Science Journal. Her purpose in founding it was "to bring to many a household health, happiness, and increased power to be good and to do good." Among its articles was one on *"the fallacy of that tired feeling,"* and surely there are readers of today to whom this might appeal. Only one poem by Mary was included in an issue, and sometimes no poem appeared, but from these published verses were chosen several that have become favorite hymns in Christian Science churches.

Mary preached a sermon each Sunday, and supervised the growing Sunday School. She taught classes in her college, attended Association meetings, brought out the sixth edition of *Science and Health*, now adding a chapter: *Key to the Scriptures.*

Seven years of teaching in the Massachusetts Metaphysical College had prepared four thousand students for graduation. Mary now wanted to devote two years to a complete revision of *Science and Health;* and she also wished to consider a serious problem that had arisen in regard to her church organization.

It might be mentioned, in passing, that a medical doctor, a man of forty, had been a student in the Massachusetts Metaphysical College. His name: Ebenezer J. Foster. On November 5, 1888, Mary Baker Eddy legally adopted this man as her son and he took the name: Ebenezer J. Foster Eddy. For a time he was helpful to her, but later they were to part, and Mary erased him from her life and thought.

In 1888 her own son visited her, his apparent objective to interest her in a western gold mine. There was love between them, though they were never spiritually close.

In 1891, with the 50th edition of *Science and Health* (very similar to the edition in use today) ready for the press, with her Massachusetts Metaphysical College temporarily closed, Mary felt the time had come to deal with her serious church problem.

She was aware that certain of her pastors were trying to create a large personal following with a view to starting churches of their own. Their sermons contained statements of which Mary did not approve, and often these pastors neglected to emphasize her own teachings. This must cease! *Her own teaching, in pure form, must be preserved!*

At Mrs. Eddy's request, the organization of her church was dissolved.

Mary bought a house near Concord, seventy miles from Boston, and went into seclusion. The house, which was named Pleasant View, had wide, beautiful grounds and many rooms. Seated at her desk in her study, Mary asked God's help in solving the problem of establishing her church on a firm foundation.

God's answer came. She was to formulate a little "Rules and By-laws" book, to be known as the *Manual of the Mother Church*. Throughout the coming centuries this little Manual would be used wherever Christian Science was taught and practiced.

The Manual is a masterpiece. It stated that Christian Science Churches would have, instead of pastors, two Readers. From the pulpit one Reader would read passages from the Bible, and the other passages from *Science and Health*. These passages would be identical for all churches on the same Sunday. The Manual set forth rules for Sunday School workers, for Librarians in Reading Rooms, for practically every situation that might arise, now or in the future.

Mary organized the church under a deed of trust in 1892, and turned over to four trustees a lot she owned at the corner of Falmouth and Norway Streets in Boston. The trustees pledged themselves to erect upon this lot a church building and Mary decided to reorganize the Boston church as a

Mother Church, with membership drawn from Christian Scientists throughout the world. The decision to build this church took place at a meeting in October, 1893, when Mary was seventy-two years old; and her request for funds for the building caused donations to pour in from her followers.

The church was completed in time for the first service to be held on December 30, 1894. Its high dome, beautiful skylight, stained glass windows, pews cushioned in old-rose plush, lent the church a "bright sense," reminding its Christian Science worshippers that happiness played an important role in this new religion. During that first service more than eleven hundred men and women filled pews and overflowed into spaces along the walls.

Pleasant View in Concord, New Hampshire, was not far from Bow, where Mary was born. She arose each morning at six in summer, seven in the winter, and breakfasted at eight o'clock. Dinner was at twelve sharp, the evening meal at six, and those who lived in the house with her were expected to be on time for meals, without benefit of gong. Immediately after dinner, the coachman would bring her carriage with its two fine horses to the front door, and Mary and Mr. Frye would take a drive, her only recreation of the day.

These drives, through snowy winter streets, beneath blue skies of spring and summer, between crimson autumn trees, were much enjoyed. Citizens of Concord watched for her coming, and collected smiles from Mary Baker Eddy.

Visitors found her never too busy for a few words of counsel. She warned against harboring enmity against those who believed in other creeds.

She always dressed becomingly, sometimes in black and white, with a short cape flung about her shoulders. Her hair, fingernails, clothing, she kept up to the "highest point of perfection."

Her sense of humor was an endearing trait. One cannot read *Science and Health* without meeting, now and then, a sentence revealing her as a gay and happy human being who enjoyed a smile.

In 1898 Mary carefully selected twenty-six topics to be used for Lesson-Sermons. These were to last, one a week, for twenty-six weeks; then the first topic would be used again and the list once more completed. Thus all fifty-two weeks of the year would be planned for. Of these twenty-six topics, Mary said: "The original subjects were given of God—they are sufficient, and they will remain forever."

The list may be found in a little magazine published every three months, the *Christian Science Quarterly*, and the topics are: God, Sacrament, Life, Truth, etc.

Churches were now opened in Canada, Europe, South America, and hundreds of Christian Science practitioners were listed in the *Journal*. In 1898 Mary started a weekly magazine, the Christian Science Journal; and in 1899 the Metaphysical College reopened as auxiliary to the church, with an auxiliary to the College called the Board of Education of the Mother Church of Christ, Scientist, in Boston, Massachusetts. On June 10, 1906, an extension of the Mother Church was dedicated, the extension holding five thousand people.

Then, on October 28, 1906, a New York newspaper published a sensational story to the effect that Mary Baker Eddy was incapable of handling her own affairs and that "others" were influencing her. Mrs. Eddy, acting calmly and without fear, decided to select three capable businessmen to take care of her property. She placed one hundred and twenty-five

thousand dollars in trust for her son and his family, and this
trust deed was signed February 25, 1907. Prior to this time
her lawyer had been General Frank S. Streeter, a very able
attorney, not a Christian Scientist, and to him she turned
for present legal advice.

Now her son, George Washington Glover II, came into
the case and on March 1, 1907, filed a "Petition of Next
Friends" advocating that a receiver be appointed to protect
Mrs. Eddy's business interests because she was in "a feeble
mental state." The "next friends" recorded in the petition
were her son's eldest child, her nephew, George W. Baker,
and her adopted son, Ebenezer Foster Eddy, as well as
George W. Glover II.

The Court, hearing the case, appointed a Judge, a doctor
and an alienist, to call upon Mrs. Eddy and examine her
health and mental capacity. Mary, now eighty-six, received
the men at Pleasant View and chatted with them easily, surprising all three with her knowledge of finance, public affairs, even international questions. She told them she still
wrote or dictated countless daily letters pertaining to her
property and her church organization; and there were few
hours between seven in the morning and her nine o'clock
bedtime at night when she was not at work.

Not only did all three men gain a favorable impression of
her mental and physical well-being, but the "Next Friends"
counsel actually asked for a dismissal of the suit. Newspapers,
agreeing that Mary Baker Eddy had been wrongfully accused, praised her for her handling of the situation.

At Mrs. Eddy's suggestion the Trustees bought for her,
the next summer, a twenty-five room house on twelve acres
in Chestnut Hill, near Boston. After the house had been re-
modelled to suit her needs, she moved there on January 26,
1908; and at Chestnut Hill continued to work long daily

hours, also to enjoy her accustomed drive between one and two each afternoon.

For many years Mrs. Eddy had given thought to the idea of publishing a daily newspaper, and now she decided to convert this idea into reality. She told the Trustees to start a newspaper and call it The Christian Science Monitor.

On November 26, 1908 *The Christian Science Monitor* appeared for the first time on the streets and since that day the *Monitor*, whose motto is: "To injure no man, but to bless all mankind" has become one of the world's most important news sheets. It is remarkable to consider that when Mrs. Eddy started this newspaper she was eighty-seven years old.

Her book *Science and Health*, was now read and re-read by those interested in serious books, as well as by her followers. Perhaps it might have surprised some readers to discover, on page 444, lines 7 to 10, that in an emergency, when necessary, a Christian Scientist may seek medical aid. Mrs. Eddy writes: "If Christian Scientists ever fail to receive aid from other Scientists,—their brethren upon whom they may call,—God will guide them into the right use of temporary and eternal means."

Mrs. Eddy, to the end of her life here on earth, had great respect for punctuality and for making the best of each moment. She declared that all successful individuals have become successful by improving moments before they pass into hours.

Her Chestnut Hill study was equipped with a system of bells, and each worker responded to a definite ring, four bells summoning them all. She sometimes called all her workers together for a talk, and often impressed upon them that if a Christian Scientist allowed God to guide his every thought and action, he'd never feel weariness in well doing, but would know happiness and peace.

On December 1, 1910, Mrs. Eddy took her usual drive, accompanied by Mr. Frye. It was a clear, frosty day, and groups of people along the road waved to her, watched for her smile, saw her lift her hand in greeting.

Next day she did not go out, but talked with her workers in her study, and they noted her slight weakness. Next day, Saturday, December 3, she remained in the house and at a quarter to eleven that night she passed on.

When news of her passing was announced the next morning (Sunday) in Christian Science churches, a message from her was read. Mary had written the message years before to explain her retirement to Concord, and it said, in part:

MY BELOVED STUDENTS:—You may be looking to see me in my accustomed place with you, but this you must no longer expect. When I retired from the field of labor, it was a departure, socially, publicly, and finally, from the routine of such material modes as society and our societies demand. . . . You can well afford to give me up, since you have in my last revised edition of *Science and Health* your teacher and guide.

Mary Baker Eddy was buried at Mount Auburn, near Boston. Newspapers throughout the land paid tribute to her life and work.

The exact number of members of the Mother Church is never published. But Christian Scientists, the world over, must number in hundreds of thousands.

Mary began it all with her first student, Hiram Crafts, in 1867; and Christian Science churches stand today in Kenya, Hong Kong, Tasmania, in North and South America and Europe. How many copies of *Science and Health* are read openly in Christian countries? How many are perhaps read secretly in Russia and Red China?

"Someday I'll write a book," said young Mary Baker long ago, in New Hampshire.

Well.

She *did*.

6

EMMA LAZARUS
(1849-1887)

The poem engraved in bronze on the interior wall of the Statue of Liberty's pedestal has been read by millions unfamiliar with the life and work of the Jewish girl who wrote it. Here is the poem:

The New Colossus

Not like the brazen giant of Greek fame,
With conquering limbs astride from land to land;
Here at our sea-washed, sunset gate shall stand
A mighty woman with a torch; whose flame
Is the imprisoned lightning; and her name
Mother of Exiles. From her beacon-hand
Glows world-wide welcome, her mild eyes command
The air-bridged harbor that twin cities frame.
"Keep, ancient lands, your storied pomp!" cries she
With silent lips. "Give me your tired, your poor,
Your huddled masses yearning to breathe free,
The wretched refuse of your teeming shore,
Send these, the homeless tempest-tost, to me,
I lift my lamp beside the golden door!"

One might imagine that the writer of these words, Emma Lazarus, had experienced poverty, hunger and hardship. Yet she was wealthy. Her Jewish ancestors had come to America in the seventeenth century; and so she knew nothing of the exile's homelessness. In imagination, however, she could put herself within the shoes of the most wretched newcomer, wear his ragged clothes, feel his hunger, know the longings of his heart. "Her deep feelings for others," Emma's sister Josephine tells us, "was due to her quick intuition, like second-sight in its sensitiveness to apprehend and respond to external stimulus."

The New Colossus and other Lazarus poems so eulogize freedom that readers unfamiliar with her life might think she had not known it herself. This, too, is an illusion. Few human beings have ever possessed more complete personal freedom than was enjoyed by this girl.

She had a happy childhood. During nine months of each school year she and her five sisters and one brother studied at home in New York City under private tutors. When the hot weather came, Emma's parents whisked the children out of the crowded city to their seaside home at Newport, R. I., so that toy sailboats might be blown by ocean breezes and castles built of white, moist sand. Emma was rich in playmates at Newport, for the Lazarus children were great friends and good at making up new games; and parental discipline, while ever in the background, gave them no consciousness of recreational restraint.

Later, during the late teens and early twenties, when the average girls fall in love and dream of marriage, Emma fell in love with poetry and dreamed of winning Ralph Waldo Emerson's praise. She spent daily hours at her desk writing long poems: *Admetus, Tannhauser, Phantasies.*

As the years went on, she enjoyed continued freedom from

problems usually tossed into a woman's life. Not for Emma
Lazarus were duties of wifehood, motherhood, home and
husband management. She was the undisputed mistress of her
every daily hour, and family wealth had swept those hours
clear of need of money-making. She possessed huge blocks of
time.

The astonishing thing was her attitude toward work. She
rigidly scheduled daily hours and converted them into poems.
"Much must be done before the brief light dies." She wrote
this as a young woman, and it was unintentionally prophetic,
for Emma died at the age of thirty-eight.

Her poem in praise of work might have been penned yesterday for today's psychology-conscious world:

> But when she fills her days with duties done
>   Strange vigor comes, she is restored to health.
> New aims, new interests rise with each new sun,
>   And life still holds for her unbounded wealth.
> All that seemed hard and toilsome now proves small,
> And naught may daunt her—she hath strength for all.

Much has been written of the love between Emma and her
father, but it was no more than natural affection between
parent and responsive child. Moses Lazarus would take her,
as a small girl, upon his knee; he'd tell her stories, recite
poems, that all good mothers and fathers tell and recite to children who will listen. Emma's response touched him deeply.
Later he took joy in teaching her to read; and still later engaged tutors not only to instruct her in literature, mathe-
matics, Greek, Latin, but to give her a thorough grounding
in French and German.

She was eleven when the Civil War broke out, and could
not help but hear talk of it. The young sons of her father's

friends, wearing blue uniforms, came to say good-bye. Presently the mothers of these boys were bringing letters to read to Emma's mother, and tears were shed. Later, two or three of the mothers brought telegrams that plunged the whole Lazarus household into grief. All this dropped into Emma's memory and later emerged, touched with magic, in her poetry.

Emma's father owned a sugar refining business. His ancestors, Sephardic Jews, had fled their native Portugal in 1497 to avoid the Spanish Inquisition that sought to convert them to Christianity. They fled to Holland, to the West Indies, later to London. After two hundred years, their descendants migrated to the New World.

Moses Lazarus kept an orthodox house and was a member of the fashionable Congregation Shearith Israel in New York City; but his faith, as old as that of the first Moses, did not flame with the passion of Judaism that had inspired his persecuted forebears. Nothing here had served to ignite that flame. He practiced his inherited religion serenely. His was a well-ordered, smooth-running life.

Emma, growing up in this calm atmosphere, accepted her father's religion as she accepted the home he provided for his family. She observed the necessary forms, kept Jewish feast and fast days, but until she was sixteen she did not give deep and serious thought to the history and meaning of the Jewish idea.

Soon after her sixteenth birthday her father retired from business. He was fifty-two, and the year was 1865. He had now accumulated sufficient wealth to enable him to turn from its pursuit to the pursuit of a good life. His retirement gave him time to visit art galleries, to hear fine music, to attend New York's many theaters, to talk with friends. He could supervise the education of his children, a task he thoroughly relished. If, as has been said, "happiness consists of thinking interesting thoughts," Moses Lazarus had retired to happiness.

He read Shakespeare and Milton with Emma, and her depth of understanding surprised him. Now and then she handed him some of her own verses for criticism, and he praised her choice of words. Her mind was ever reaching out toward truth-discovery, a trait that delighted her father. He not only urged her to write more, but suggested that she try to translate the poems of Heine, Dumas, Hugo into English. Someday he'd have her original poems, as well as her translations, printed in a little book for distribution among relatives and friends.

One can imagine Moses Lazarus' pride in this beautiful six-teen-year-old daughter as they strolled along New York's streets in 1865, when that city with its half million population had for them so much of interest. Emma, of medium height, with a patrician-oval face, with dark glossy hair and darker eyes, carried herself proudly. The way she'd bound her hair with a neat dark ribbon, the way she wore her white-collared, full-skirted, chic blue silk dress, gave her such distinction that passers-by stared. She did not notice. Her thoughts were on her conversation with her father.

People could tell he was her father. There was a marked resemblance. The same dark hair, fine dark eyes, well-defined features, olive complexion. Both wore the imprint of long ago Sephardic ancestors, and but for their modern, well-cut clothes, they might have been walking along a street in Lisbon, Portugal.

Wealth accumulated by those ancestors had cushioned today for Moses and Emma Lazarus. They lived in fashionable Union Square. They walked the best streets. A few blocks away from them dwelt people facing the bitter reality of poverty, people who lived in wretched lodgings, who ate poor food, who searched daily and in vain for work. Emma and Moses Lazarus knew them not. As yet.

They stood a moment to admire the new Woman's Hospital at the Corner of Park Avenue and 50th Street; and of course they had no way of knowing that, on that same spot, would one day stand the Waldorf Astoria Hotel. They walked along 50th street to Fifth Avenue, strolled down to 42nd street where stood the Reservoir, on the very corner where today stands New York's great Library. There were no tall buildings, and Moses and Emma did not visualize them, yet such were even then in the making. A newly invented "safe elevator" run by steam had just been installed in a five-story building on Broadway. Later, run by electricity, the elevator would make possible the skyscraper.

At the end of each block, when they wanted to cross the street, Emma and Moses had to wait for horse-drawn cabs, stages, street-cars to pass. The clatter of the horses' hoofs upon cobblestoned pavement would drown out their voices and force them to save what they were saying till they reached the sidewalk.

Moses said: "I understand we're to be introduced to a new mode of living. The French Flat, or *apartment*, as some people call it. It's an arrangement whereby several families all live under the same roof, separated by partitions. Each family has its own kitchen, bedroom, and so on."

Emma's expressive face showed unbelief. "You can't be serious, father."

"Oh, but I am. And someday there may be thousands of such buildings in New York, who knows? I've a feeling that the younger married people may like them. If I weren't fifty-two I might be tempted to build one. Just as an experiment, mind you. A gamble in human nature."

"No doubt you'd win, Father. You usually do."

He laughed and they walked on together in silence. Wonderful to be alive in this era of change. Each day a new world to explore.

It was during the next year, when Emma was seventeen, that she discovered the writings of Emerson. She was already familiar with Goethe. She found in Goethe's work such sage advice as: "Treat people as if they were what they ought to be." Emerson said: "Trust men and they will be true to you; treat them greatly and they will show themselves great."

She discovered in Emerson a "mine of wisdom and goodness." "A friend must possess two all-important attributes: *tenderness* and *sincerity*." "Every revolution was first a thought in one man's mind; every reform a private opinion." During the years that she was seventeen and eighteen she read Emerson avidly. He kept lighting for her little truth-candles.

Her father, true to his promise, had published a small volume of her poems and translations, and this little book, bearing Emma's name, was prized and praised by her relatives. Their praise did not excite her. She knew she could write much better now.

One evening, just before her nineteenth birthday, her father took her with him to the home of a banker friend, Samuel Gray Ward. In the living room were several elderly men seated in easy chairs, smoking cigars, discussing the topics of the day; and as her father introduced Emma to one and then another, she bowed politely and murmured a word of greeting. She'd noted a bookcase in a corner and a bench beside it. In imagination, she had already seated herself there.

Suddenly her ears caught a name, and she looked quickly into the smiling face of the man in a deep cushioned chair. He had keen observing eyes. His hair was white. Emma's father was saying:

"Emma, my dear. This is Mr. Ralph Waldo Emerson."

She bowed to him. She felt her cheeks grow warm. She dared not trust her voice.

"My daughter has already had a small book published," said Moses Lazarus.

Emma flushed deeply. What would the Sage of Concord think of a book by an eighteen-year-old girl? But sixty-five year old Ralph Waldo Emerson's handsome face was utterly serious as he told her he would like to read it. Would she please send him a copy?

After she'd moved away and gone to sit beside the bookcase, she felt alive and excited as never before in her life. His request held wonder in it, almost unbelief. He would read her poems! As she sat there, the room with its cigar smoke and many voices scarcely existed. She had embarked upon a mental journey to Concord and was watching the Great Man take a package from his mailbox.

She mailed her book of poems, with a letter, to Mr. Emerson on February 12, 1868. And after twelve days of watchful waiting, she received his verdict. He thought that perhaps she'd used too sad a theme in some of her poems. And she needed more economy of words. For lessons in economy, why not re-read Shakespeare? But he thought that Emma's poems were good. He liked them.

Reading his letter again and again in the privacy of her bedroom, Emma felt her heart beat with warm pride and pleasure. He'd liked her poems! She lifted her head and stared into a bright imagine future. She would send him more and more poetry and he'd criticise her verses. She'd learn economy of words, and learn to earn his praise. What was it he had said of friendship? A friend is *tender* and *sincere*. She placed his letter in a carved wooden treasure chest on her bureau, telling herself that its words contained these qualities in generous measure.

She went to the bookcase and took down Emerson's essay

on Friendship. Before a friend, one might think aloud without dissimulation, without second thought. A friend was a comfort through all the relations of life. Emma studied these words a moment, then glanced at her reflection in the bureau mirror. She smiled into her own dark eyes.

During the next two years, she exchanged letters with Emerson and began to depend upon his advice and criticism, also to accept a share of his philosophy. He told her to read Thoreau and Whitman. He pointed out that a poet relates past to present in such a way that the reader may discover in the poem a truth to be used in his own life.

Emerson was deeply interested in a doctrine known as Transcendentalism, which preached that every man has God within him, and should listen to the voice of God within himself. This philosophy, which emphasized the "living God in the soul," preached the worth of the individual, and was concerned with intuition, inspiration, and spiritual matters outside of human experience. A touch of this "God within us" doctrine no doubt found itself into Emma's subconscious during this period of her life when she regarded Emerson with great respect and awe.

She had been corresponding with him for a few months when she invited him to visit her home, and her father added a postscript to the invitation assuring him that he should be "master of the situation" at all times, and have complete privacy. Pressure of work prevented Emerson's acceptance, much to Emma's disappointment.

But their letters continued, and she asked him many questions which he did his best to answer. She gave him her views upon various subjects, and if he deemed her wrong, he told her so and why. She thought of their correspondence as "conversation" because, according to the Greeks, conversation is "the supreme art of discovering the truth."

His remarks on Transcendentalism gave her a new interest in her own religion, Judaism, and she began to compare the two. Of course Judaism was far, far more than mere form and ceremony. It was a quality of the soul. She saw that the highest duty in all religions was love. God's love made humanity whole.

At the age of eighteen she'd written: "In the Jewish Synagogue at Newport," a poem in which she mentioned "the perpetual lamp," "Eastern towns and temples," "the Patriarch and his flocks," "Jehovah's written law," and so on. All this revealed Emma's awareness of kinship with her own Jewish heritage.

In September 1868, when she was nineteen, Emma wrote a very long poem, "Admetus" and sent it to Mr. Emerson for criticism. She had inscribed the poem: "To my friend, Ralph Waldo Emerson."

Time went by and no letter with a Concord postmark came. Hadn't he liked *Admetus?* Was he, for some reason, angry with her? Why didn't he write? She wrote in her diary: "Another no-letter day. How long can I endure them?"

September melted into October. Still no letter from him. What was wrong? The distance from her home to Concord was about two hundred miles, but in 1868, by train or stage coach, the journey required days. Telegrams had not yet become a mode of social correspondence, and it was not until March 10, 1876, that Alexander Graham Bell spoke the very first words ever transmitted by telephone: "Mr. Watson, come here, I need you." So young Emma Lazarus, her world turning dull and gray, had to be content to watch and wait.

At last, on October 28, Emerson wrote that he was "dipping into the poem." He had received it, then. Surely it would not be too long a time before she had his verdict.

But it was a long time. Another month and not a word. Did he disapprove of *Admetus* but hesitate to tell her so because she'd worked upon it so hard? But no. That would not be like him. He had always shared with her, in complete frankness, all his thought about her verses.

On November 22nd, Emerson's son, Edward Waldo Emerson, delivered *Admetus* to her door, with a letter from his father. She invited him into the living room, but while they sat talking she scarcely heard a word the young man said, so eager was Emma to open his father's letter. The moment the visitor had gone, she tore the envelope and took out Emerson's "verdict" with trembling fingers. She read: "You have written a noble poem which I cannot enough praise."

She sat down in an easy chair and felt that no one could possibly measure her happiness. For a time she sat very still, then re-read the words: "a noble poem which I cannot enough praise." Presently she arose, went to her desk, and wrote to him. She said she'd been as much astonished as delighted at his estimate of her poem, and that his praise would spur her to better writing. She signed the note, addressed the envelope, then took *Admetus* from its wrapping and read it again. Now, in the light of Ralph Waldo Emerson's praise, the poem really did seem rather good.

The poem was about Admetus, King of Thessaly, who fell in love with the beautiful Alcestis whose hair resembled "soft undulations of warm gold." The girl's father had declared she might wed no man unless he could "beard and bind the lion, tame the boar, drive wild beasts before his chariot." Once in love with Alcestis, Admetus did all this with the help of a God, Hyperion. Then he and Alcestis were married.

Soon after the birth of their son, Admetus became very ill, and the beautiful Alcestis, his wife, heard a voice say, "A

God dwells within you; seek and you shall find." Alcestis sought the God, Hyperion, who in turn sought the Fates. The Fates promised to spare Admetus' life in exchange for the life of someone else.

The lovely Alcestis offered her life for that of her husband, but when Death came to claim her, Hyperion wrestled with Death and won. Admetus recovered his health, and he and the beautiful Alcestis and their child lived happily ever after.

Beneath the poem's surface lay its meaning. A wife might consider it her duty to give up her life for her husband. But life itself is God, and thus not really hers to give up. Because of "God within us," a wife's life is of equal importance to that of her husband, *and so must be lived*.

Emma Lazarus had not been reading Ibsen's *A Doll's House*, for that great play was as yet unwritten. The philosophy in "Admetus" was entirely her own.

In 1871, when Emma was twenty-two, *Admetus and Other Poems* was published in book form, and well received in the United States. In England the book, particularly its poem "Admetus" was praised very highly. Certain English critics declared "Admetus" to be superior to many of the poems written by the great Robert Browning.

She now wrote a romantic novel dealing with a love affair in the life of the great German writer, Goethe. The title was *Alide* and this book came out early in 1874. She sent a copy to the Russian writer, Turgenev, then in Paris, and he not only read it but wrote at once to Emma: "I am truly glad to say, Miss Lazarus, that I have read your book with the liveliest interest. It is very sincere, and very poetical at the same time. . . . Your characters are drawn with a pencil as delicate as it is strong. . . . An author who writes as you do is not a "pupil in art" any more; he is not far from being himself a master."

But in the Fall of 1874, Emma received a severe blow. Emerson had collected an anthology of more than 500 pages of verse by more than 165 poets, thirty-eight of whom were Americans. He had entitled the book: *Parnassus.* Emma at once bought a copy and eagerly scanned it for her own name and one of her poems. He had not mentioned Emma Lazarus.

She could not believe it. Hadn't he meant the praise he'd given "Admetus," and her other verses? She felt betrayed.

Her father tried to ease her pain. He quoted: "Everything matters a little, nothing matters much." He told her that ten years from now she'd look back and smile at this. He carefully scanned the list of names in *Parnassus.* "Look here, my darling. He's left out Whitman and Poe. He's left out Swinburne."

But Emma would not be comforted. She showed her father that Emerson, in his preface, had explained that not all of the poems had been listed for their general merit. Some of them were there because a line, or even a word had impressed him. Apparently, then, not even a line or a word of hers had impressed him in the least.

Moses Lazarus put an arm about his daughter. "Emma, my dear, didn't the great Turgenev himself tell you that you were not far from being a master? The important thing is not to see your name listed in *Parnassus,* but to know *that you can write.*"

Emma kissed her father. But her wound was not assuaged. She went to her desk and wrote to Emerson. Was his omission of her name a public retraction of the very flattering opinions he had sent her? Would he please explain? She sealed the letter and addressed it to R. W. Emerson, Esquire. There is no record of his reply.

Life went on for Emma Lazarus, and by dint of hard daily work at her desk she managed to put *Parnassus* out of her thoughts. In the Spring of 1876 her mother died, and with her passing went Emma's feeling of youth. She and Sarah, her older sister, now must mother the younger members of the family and comfort their bereaved father.

Mr. Emerson, learning of her mother's death, and perhaps thinking to divert her mind to some degree from her great loss, invited Emma to spend a week in Concord. She went at the end of August and Mr. Emerson himself met her at the Concord station and drove her in his "little one-horse wagon" to his "gray square house with dark blinds, set among noble trees."

She was welcomed warmly by Mrs. Emerson and their daughter, Ellen, ten years older than Emma, and shown to the bedroom that was to be hers for an entire week. As she unpacked her dresses and hung them in the mahogany wardrobe, she must have felt high excitement. Seven days of conversation with the Sage of Concord himself!

She at once made friends with Ellen and her mother, and she was completely charmed with the details of the Emerson household. The family breakfasts, Emerson's rigidly scheduled hours in his study, during which no one, under any circumstances disturbed him; the callers who dropped in during late afternoons and stayed to dinner, all this was like reading a novel that had come to life.

During their walks together over the country roads and along the banks of the quiet river. she gradually became better acquainted with Ralph Waldo Emerson. She saw that this tall, spare, white-haired, still handsome seventy-three year old man was growing somewhat forgetful. And now, eight years wiser than had been the worshipping girl who was herself at nineteen, she observed in him a trait she'd not then suspected.

His strong religious views colored his personal estimate of the work of a writer. If that work corresponded with his own philosophy, he tended to magnify its merits. Perhaps her "Admetus" had failed to strike the exact inspirational note that stirred and matched his inner sensibilities. Emma could accept this explanation now, and smile.

While Emerson worked in his study, Emma walked and talked with Mr. William Ellery Channing, Emerson's friend and neighbor. Afterward, in her diary, she described Mr. Channing as "odd but of noble character," but during their long conversations at Concord she gave him her undivided attention. He told her stories of the late Henry Thoreau, who had been his best friend, showed her Thoreau's pond, and the place where he had built his little hut. He pointed out the log on which he and Thoreau sat and talked of the average man who, Thoreau declared, led a "life of quiet desperation." "Then what of the life of the average woman?" Emma wanted to know. But William Ellery Channing was not to be led down paths of feminine speculation. He firmly anchored conversation upon Thoreau.

Mr. Channing was too elderly, too eccentric, to hold for Emma even a slight flicker of romantic interest. But in her manuscript journal she described Concord's quiet beauty, its sunlight slanting through the trees, the "blue and silver summer sky that seemed to shed, over all, an exquisite peace." If, during those August days, when she'd forsaken her desk and had entered into a holiday mood, there'd been an eligible young man about Concord, who knows what romantic turn her life-story might have taken?

It has been said that one returns from a vacation a different person, and it was true that Emma Lazarus came home from Concord with a new outlook. Her discerning eyes had seen Ralph Waldo Emerson, not as an idol, but as a fallible human being.

No, he was not infallible, yet she still deeply respected his judgment, and had left in Concord with him the proof-sheets of her new play in five acts, *The Spagnoletto*, a tragedy laid in the year 1655 in Italy. What would he think of it? Eagerly, she awaited his verdict.

But letter-writing had become a burden to him, and he now left that task, as far as possible, to his daughter, Ellen. Emma heard from Ellen that her father had begun reading of *The Spagnoletto* and was unable to put it down. Emma took a deep breath of triumph. Imagine the great Emerson *having* to read all five acts of her play at one sitting!

Later, Emerson pointed out that "every word and line of *The Spagnoletto* told of richness in the poetry." He told her that it had held his interest in an emotional vise. It is true that, even today, the reader of *The Spagnoletto* "cannot choose but read." Somehow, it contains that suspenseful, gripping, unexplainable quality for which, decades later, motion picture studios freely paid fabulous sums.

The story has to do with a great Italian artist, Ribera, and his beautiful daughter, Maria. Ribera, known as "The Spagnoletto" is sternly protective of Maria's virtue, and tries to guard the young girl's every waking hour from suitors, desirable and undesirable. But for all his watchfulness, Ribera, being human, has to give way at night to sleep; and it is then that Maria and the handsome Prince John of Austria enjoy making love in the garden. Because of her father's over-protection, the girl falls prey to Prince John's experienced way with a maid. When the Prince's father calls him to Austria, Maria follows him blindly, without benefit of marriage. News of his daughter's dishonor causes Ribera to forsake his painting and join the priesthood. After Maria's Prince had married a Royal Princess, heartbroken Maria returns to Italy and takes refuge in a convent. At confession the Priest to whom she tells her story turns out to be her own father, and the father further punishes Maria by killing himself before her horrified eyes.

It is amazing that Emma should have invented such a plot, and remarkable that, seated at her sheltered desk, she should wander in imagination through the "storm and sweep of passion" of the garden scenes, then follow this Catholic father and daughter to their story's tragic end. But Emma was turning a revealing light upon the father-daughter relationship, and attempting to record a universal truth.

In October, 1877, the Lazarus family moved from 36 West 14th Street to 34 East 57th Street. Perhaps Moses Lazarus could not endure the memories of his beloved wife in the home they'd shared for more than twenty years.

Once settled in the new house, Emma began her excellent translations of the poems of Heinrich Heine, who died when Emma herself was seven. The brilliant young Jew, with "the mind and eyes of a Greek," was born in 1799 in Dusseldorf, Germany, wrote ballads, travel sketches, volumes of prose and some of the world's most tender and beautiful love lyrics. He died at the age of fifty-six.

On her desk, Emma kept a picture of the young Heine, whom someone had called the German Byron, and the picture showed a beardless blond young man with oval face, dimple in chin, dark eyes that "held a thousand beauty-dreams." Emma had read everything he'd written.

As she explored the details of his career, before writing a brief sketch of his life, he became as real to her as was the man next door, or her publisher, or Emerson himself. In imagination she went with Heine to the French monastery during the day, to the private Jewish school he attended in the late afternoon and evening. When he was nineteen and his millionaire uncle, Solomon Heine, gave him opportunity to learn the mercantile business in Hamburg, Emma all but heard the uncle tell Heine's father that the "fool of a boy" would never make a business man, but should try to get a law degree at Hamburg University.

While attending Hamburg University, Heine fell madly, hopelessly in love with Solomon Heine's daughter, and Emma felt that his unrequited passion for the girl not only inspired much of his poetry but gave the keynote to his whole tone and spirit. He had to "submit to Baptism as a Christian" before being allowed to graduate from the University, but he remained at heart a Jew.

He now wrote articles about liberalism, Jewish freedom from oppression and the *sacredness of labor*. He went to Paris and wrote in French his famous essays on French art and German philosophy; also he acquired the reputation of being "the wittiest Frenchman since Voltaire." He met and married a young French girl who loved him devotedly and nursed him through the illness of the last ten years of his life, those years spent upon what Heine termed his "mattress grave." Just before he died he asked to be carried to the Louvre and placed on the floor near the statue of the Venus de Milo so that he might once more see her beauty. *Here Heine wept.*

Emma's book, *Poems and Ballads of Heinrich Heine*, with a biographical sketch, was published in 1881 and was well received. She also had several of her own poems published that year, in various magazines.

Two years before, however, in 1879, in a distant province of Russia a cry had arisen against the Jews and a series of cruel pogroms had taken place. Province after province echoed the cry, and Jewish persecution spread from Russia to Bulgaria, Servia and Roumania. Stories of savage beatings, robbery, rape, found their way in 1880, with documented evidence, to newspapers in London. Weeks later these stories reached the United States and Emma Lazarus, picking up the

New York Times one morning, read that half a million Jews had been slaughtered and their property, worth untold millions of dollars, had been destroyed. She read that countless thousands of Jews were destitute and homeless.

As she read, Emma felt this persecution in every cell of her body, for *these were her people*. She took the paper to her father and they read it together. There must be something they could do!

Emma attended a mass meeting in New York where the Secretary of State, Mr. William Evarts, said: "It is not that it is the oppression of Jews by Russia; it is that it is the oppression of men and women by men and women; and we are men and women." Yes, cried Emma Lazarus, silently.

The mass meeting was attended by people representing various religious faiths: Catholics, Jews, Protestants. All stood united in protest against this shameful treatment of those of Jewish faith; and they pledged their time, money and labor in an effort to help.

Emma now had a crusade to which she dedicated all her time, almost her every thought. It was not that she'd suddenly awakened to a Jewish consciousness, for she had always been intensely conscious of and interested in her Jewish ancestors and background. It was that she realized she had not learned nearly enough about that background's history, and about the spiritual meaning of Judaism.

A few years before, she had written an Historical Play in Five Acts entitled, *The Dance of Death,* a tragedy set in the year 1349 and dealing with the burning on a funeral pyre of hundreds of German Jews falsely blamed for bringing the Black Death upon Christiandom. In 1882 this play, with other poems by Emma Lazarus, was published in pamphlet form under the title: *Songs of a Semite.*

She dedicated *The Dance of Death* to the memory of

George Eliot, who had died in 1880, after writing the 1,490-page novel, Daniel Deronda. In this novel, Miss Eliot had given her Jewish hero this speech: "I am going to the East to become better acquainted with the condition of my race in the various countries there. *The idea that I am possessed with is that of restoring a political existence to my people, making them a nation again, giving them a national center, such as the English have, though they, too, are scattered over the face of the globe. That is a task which presents itself as a duty. I am resolved to begin it, however feebly. I am resolved to devote my life to it. At the very least, I may awaken a movement in other minds, such as has been awakened in my own.*"

Emma, with George Eliot, saw that the solution to the Jewish problem was this: the Jews should have a country of their own. The idea grew and developed in her mind, and she determined that, like Daniel Deronda, she would dedicate herself to the realization of this idea: *A homeland for the Jews.*

Now she began to make an intensive study of Jewish history, and in order to research in the original language of her people, she learned Hebrew. Within a few months she was able to read Hebrew with ease.

She read in Hebrew the story of Abraham, the father of her race, whose ancestor, Heber, was responsible for the name "Hebrews." Abraham's grandson, Jacob, had his name changed to Israel by God, thus the national name: Israelites. Jacob's son, Judah, was ancestor of David and Jesus; but the term *Jew* was derived from Judaeus, about 586.

Bible stories now "came alive" for Emma: Moses leading his people out of the wilderness and writing the Ten Commandments; Joshua establishing the Israelites in the Land of Promise. After Joshua came the council of elders, then the judges, then the kings. The first king was Saul, then David, then Solomon; and Solomon's son saw part of his kingdom secede, and later the kingdom itself divided into northern Israel and southern Judea.

She read that one after another of Israel's kings were then assassinated until the Kingdom of Israel itself ended in 921 B.C. The Kingdom of Judea, with its Temple established in Jerusalem by Solomon, was invaded by Babylon and Egypt, and the Temple itself fell before Nebuchadnezzar in 525 B.C.

Half a century later, the Israelites managed to return to Palestine, build a second Temple, and establish a Commonwealth that lasted for 586 years until, in 70 A.D., Titus conquered Palestine, destroyed the Temple and drove the Israelites out.

The Israelites, driven from Palestine, followed trade routes east, west, north, south, and even with their political life gone, they somehow maintained a national consciousness and handed down the Jewish faith, law, and philosophy intact from generation to generation. They taught their children Abraham's conception of one God, Daniel's Messiah prophecy, and all the rest.

During periods of persecution, each individual to the best of his ability sustained the other, thus helping to forge a bond of brotherhood. Persecution at times served to stunt the Jews physically, but it increased their religious fervor and stimulated their thirst for knowledge.

Emma read the almost unbelievable stories of banishment. England banished Jews for 365 years: from 1290 to 1665. France expelled them in 1394, and the Spanish Inquisition of 1492 drove them from Spain and Portugal. Venice passed in 1516 its inhuman laws declaring boundaries of ghettoes, and these cruel laws spread throughout Europe, culminating in Russia's 1879 pogroms.

The American Revolution of 1776 gave Jews civil and political freedom and equality, as did the French Revolution thirteen years later. England, in 1866, lifted legal restrictions against the participation of Jews in public affairs, and in Germany, after the wars of 1866 and 1870, Jews and Christians were placed upon an equal legal footing before the law.

Emma knew that Jewish Synagogues were always built exactly as in ancient days, with the entrance facing east, reader's desk in the middle bearing tall candlesticks, the perpetual lamp burning before the tabernacle containing scrolls of the law. These scrolls, wrapped in silk, are over-topped with silvery tinkling bells. Men, with heads covered, sit in the main part of the synagogue, white and blue-bordered silken scarfs over their shoulders, the fringes of the scarfs knotted according to custom to represent Hebrew characters of the law as set forth in the first five books of the Old Testament. The service, entirely in Hebrew, is chanted by the reader, with response by the congregation. Occasionally there is a chorus of male voices. Women sit in the gallery.

It thrilled Emma to remember, while seated in the gallery of her synagogue, that this scene had been unchanged for centuries. Man's ways and customs upon earth have greatly changed. A Jew of 400 B.C., returned to life today, would marvel at our trains, planes, man-made moons. But once inside a synagogue, he'd feel at home.

She read again the life of Moses Mendelssohn, born in Germany in 1729, brought up in the extreme formalism of the Jewish faith, who became a great scholar. Mendelssohn translated classics into Hebrew, and translated the first five books of the Old Testament into German, and thus brought into the ghetto the best thought of the day. He believed a Jew had the right of citizenship in the land of his birth, and advocated emancipation from much ceremonial law. "Jews," he said, "have a mission to be a light unto the Gentiles, and to bring salvation unto the end of the Earth."

Mendelssohn's teaching resulted in a movement toward Reformed Judaism which spread to America. His followers today are known as Reformed Jews, while those who cling to traditional law and custom are known as Orthodox Jews. A third group, between the two, are termed Conservative Jews.

Emma Lazarus, whose family had always been Orthodox Jews, now felt emotionally stirred and intellectually enriched by her study in Hebrew of Jewish history and thought. She grew conscious of a deep love for all Jews, and sensed their and her own Unity with God.

In 1880 the United States had a quarter of a million Jews among its entire population. They lived as Americans under our Constitution, and faced the future with confidence.

In 1881 and 1882 more than 200,000 persecuted Jews of Russia crossed the ocean in old and inhumanly crowded steamships and docked at New York Harbor. Emma went to the Harbor to watch them disembark.

She saw them walking slowly down the gangplank: old, young, middle-aged, children; the feeble, the sick, the healthy. Among them were black-gowned, bearded ancients. One elderly couple in out-of-date clothing, the wife wearing a head shawl, walked arm-in-arm, their very closeness perhaps assuaging apprehension. Young couples came ashore, their clinging small children wide-eyed, subdued before imagined frightening aspects of this strange shore. Young men and women, walking straight and fearlessly, sent Emma passing glances, no doubt recognizing her as one of their own.

They had come seeking refuge, but Emma's discerning eyes saw that they needed more. Much more. That groping woman must have spectacles, that stumbling man a cane; those under-nourished children with thin thin arms and legs and faces must have the right food. What could she do? These were her people, the children of God.

She had no way of knowing that grandchildren of these refugees would become leaders in America's industrial, commercial, political world. Some would win distinction as doctors, lawyers, scientists. Some would write America's songs, direct her plays, compose her poetry.

She could not foresee that descendants of these people would dwell in ultra-modern homes, drive their own cars, fly their own planes. College-educated, they'd find outlets for energies and talents, and prosper in fields of their choice.

All that Emma saw were here-and-now needs that must be supplied. Temporarily the refugees would be housed on Ward's Island. But they must be taught English; and also trades and skills by which they might earn a living. These basic needs were Emma's concern.

She began daily visits to Ward's Island, and gradually the masses of people began to divide into individuals. Among them she discovered scholars who read and spoke Greek, Hebrew, German, Russian. She met with those who were familiar with Heine's writings, and those who could discuss with her the work of Laurence Oliphant, the British diplomat who, though a Christian, was deeply concerned with Jewish problems. She discovered educated people who could neither read nor write English, and others, of all ages, who were completely illiterate. Here, on Ward's Island, a cross-section of the world!

The hours of Emma's days were now so completely crowded that one wonders when she slept. After her morning and afternoon visits to Ward's Island, she wrote poetry that sang passionately of her own people, their suffering, their exaltation. Her work published during this period: *The Banner of the Jew, An Epistle of Joshua Ibn Vives,* and *The New Year,* gave her, according to critics, "the strongest claim to foremost rank in American Literature."

When Henry Wadsworth Longfellow died (March, 1882), she was asked to write a short article about the poet and his work. This appeared in the April 14, 1882 "The American Hebrew," and while it praised him for writing with "exquisite delicacy of taste and admirable skill of workmanship," she said that he dealt with the past rather than the present or future.

After the death of Ralph Waldo Emerson (April 27, 1882), *The Century* for July, 1882, carried an essay entitled "Emerson's Personality" by Emma Lazarus. While writing this she glanced back over the years when she'd treasured his every word concerning her work, whether criticism or praise. She re-read her essay. Would he like what she had written about him? Tears sprang to her eyes. In praising him, she could only honor herself.

She now had many articles on the Jewish question published in *The American Hebrew* and *The Century,* revealing her complete candor and honesty, her high intelligence and love for humanity. Indeed, these articles give us the real Emma Lazarus.

She asks in one article the question: "Was Benjamin Disraeli, England's Prime Minister (Earl of Beaconsfield) a representative Jew?" Her answer, in effect, was that if a man is to represent a people he must possess qualities possessed by the united members of his race. Disraeli, born a Jew but baptized a Christian at the age of nine, represented his race in that he made the most of opportunity. Transplanted in him from Spanish-Jewish ancestors was fiery Castilian pride. Was he, though, *the finest type of Jew?* Such men, in all races, are rare. In her opinion, Disraeli was a sagacious politician rather than a wise statesman. Was he, therefore, a representative Jew? Yes. Was he a *first-class member of that race?* Perhaps not.

This article about Disraeli was published in the April 1882 issue of *The Century*, and in the same issue of that magazine was an article by Madame Zinaida Alexievna Ragozin, well known historian, entitled *Russian Jews and Gentiles: from a Russian Point of View.* Madame Ragozin did not apologize for the recent Russian pogroms, but wrote that there must be a reason why people turned against the Jews. Was the reason that Jews worshiped money, until money became more important to them than honor? Also, did they sometimes form a hostile "state within a state"?

Emma, as she finished reading this article, was conscious of hot anger. How unjust for Madame Ragozin to thus libel a race that had produced such men as Moses, St. Paul, the Prophets, even Jesus! Had these men placed money before honor? She went to her desk, wrote an answer to the unfair article, and her answer appeared in *The Century's* next issue.

In that answer, "Russian Christianity versus Modern Judaism" she said all loyal Americans of whatever creed protested against the Russian pogroms. She admitted that there were Jews who worshiped the "golden calf" and Gentiles, too, who loved money. All humanity contains the good, the bad. Every land has its small quota of men and women of genius, complete integrity, moral purity. It has many of average intelligence and character. And in each country a small number has low ethical standards. This is a picture of the human race, of which Jews are a part.

In refuting the charge that Jews sometimes form a hostile "state within a state," she quoted Jeremiah 29, 7. "And seek the welfare of the city whither I have banished you, and pray in its behalf unto the Lord, for in its welfare shall ye fare well." She said that this was a Jewish teaching, and that if Jews received equal legal justice in any country, they would become loyal citizens.

In another article in *The Century*, entitled "The Jewish Problem" (February 1883) she made a statement that has since been widely quoted: "Every Jew, however honorable or enlightened, has the humiliating knowledge that his security and reputation are, in a certain sense, bound up with those of the meanest rascal who belongs to his tribe, and who has it in his power to jeopardize the social status of his whole nation."

She wrote sixteen articles entitled *An Epistle to the Hebrews* and these appeared once a week in *The American Hebrew*. She emphasized here that all religions taught supremacy of the spirit over the materialistic, and advised Jews to have high ethical standards, faith in themselves and to plan and shape their lives in partnership with God and according to their own abilities and dreams.

Emma made it clear that antipathy to manual labor had become a great social disease of the age. She stirred up a tempest when she wrote: "Industrial training for Jews is more important that the Torah, the Talmud, the Hebrew language, Synagogue worship, or even circumcision." She assured her critics she hadn't meant to condemn Jewish ceremonies, but had merely intended to say that Jews must not entrench behind a Chinese wall of religious form so that they are blind to the need of their people for industrial education. She further stated that in her opinion religious ceremony, far from being neglected, should be performed daily, with spiritual awareness and fire in the heart; with "an inner voice that speaks of loving one's neighbor as one's self."

During daily hours at Ward's Island, she displayed unusual

organization ability, and soon had a long room equipped with tables, chairs, blackboards, writing materials. Refugees who could neither read nor write their own language, and knew no English, were placed under competent teachers, many of them Emma's personal friends. The refugees who already knew English were given instruction in American history and civics.

She realized that once these people became intellectually Americanized, they must acquire manual skills that would bring them a living in the labor market. Emma went to wealthy Jewish friends, also the editor of *The American Hebrew*, and "sold" her idea of building and equipping a Hebrew Technical Institute. A committee was organized to look into manual training courses given in Massachusetts Technical Institute, and also Philadelphia's Franklin Institute. And finally, after great effort and endless pleas for contributions on the part of Emma Lazarus, money was raised in New York City, and the Hebrew Technical Institute became a reality.

Once the Technical Institute opened its doors, Emma turned to another project, one even closer to her heart. This was the idea of a permanent home for the Jews in Palestine.

In February, 1883, in an article in *The Century*, she declared that Jews must establish an independent nationality. And in *The American Hebrew* she wrote that she was fully persuaded that "all suggested solutions of the Jewish problem other than the establishment of an independent nationality are but temporary palliatives." She did not urge that the Jewish people should migrate *en masse* to Palestine. But she did urge that prosperous Jews should unite now in an attempt to fulfill their historical destiny in accordance with the Bible's promise and prophecy. They should lay plans for this project and become awake to all opportunities that point toward this goal. She quoted a Chinese proverb: "The gods themselves cannot help him who ignores opportunity."

Her articles on Palestine stirred comment and even severe criticism among prominent New York Jews. One Jewish editor called her idea of restoration of Jews to Palestine a *fantasy*. A Jewish leader violently disagreed with her whole idea of a Jewish Commonwealth in Palestine, and told her that the time of fulfillment of Biblical promise and prophecy had not yet arrived.

Emma, ignoring these critics, continued her crusade. She talked about Palestine to every friend and acquaintance. She wrote to prominent Jews in other countries, asking their help. And she collected money to be used for the project; then placed this money in the hands of a Committee for the Establishment of a Jewish Homeland in Palestine."

In April, 1883, the Lazarus family moved to 18 West Tenth Street in New York City. The family consisted of Moses Lazarus, now seventy, and Emma's five sisters, as well as herself. Eliezer Frank, their brother, had already established a home of his own.

In the vigor and excitement of her Jewish-Colonization-in-Palestine idea, Emma kept wanting to meet people who agreed with her plan and could help. She knew that certain prominent British Jews could do much for her project if they would. And so she decided to go to England. On May 15, 1883, she and one of her sisters embarked on the S. S. Alaska.

She proved to be an excellent sailor, and enjoyed every moment of the voyage. She liked to stand for hours at a time at the railing, dressed in a warm woolen coat, her dark hair blowing back from her face, dark eyes gazing thoughtfully across the waves at the far horizon. What were her dreams?

Could she dream that Theodor Herzel, a Jewish boy of twenty-three, was at this very moment studying law at

Vienna's University; and that he would one day write a play: *The Jewish State?* No, of course her dreams could not know him. He was to write in that play: "Let the sovereignty be granted Jews over a portion of the globe large enough to satisfy the rightful requirements of a nation; the rest we shall manage ourselves." Years later he was to create the term "Zionism."

It is not given to human beings to see beyond today's horizon into tomorrow. But what might it have meant to the heart of Emma Lazarus to be able to foresee the State of Israel, geographically part of Asia, culturally part of Europe, historically part of the world?

In England, Emma was overwhemed with wonder and delight of new impressions. London's quaint streets reminded her of a "scene from one of Walter Scott's novels"; and when she and her sister sailed down the Thames River, she wrote to her father of the Thames' "clear gray water upon which snowy swans glided almost within touching distance."

Emma received invitations to the homes of important English Jews who questioned her at length about her plan for Palestine. Not only did they approve, but offered financial aid.

The great poet, Robert Browning, who was now enjoying at the age of seventy "the last of life for which the first was made," invited her to tea. They discussed poetry, and to her delight she discovered that he could read Hebrew. He agreed that manual dexterity would be needed in the building of a new Palestine, and declared that development of the Promised Land would require many farmers. He quoted in Hebrew one of his favorite lines from the Talmud: "A man who is not fond of agriculture can scarcely be called a man."

Emma spent a day in Surrey inspecting the furniture factory of famous William Morris, a handsome, bearded, forty-nine-year old poet and architect. Later she was to write an article about this visit. Morris introduced her to his friend, Burne-Jones, the artist whose exquisite painting, *The Golden Stairs*, has become immortal, and will never grow old.

In July, Emma and her sister went to Paris, arriving there on July 14th, Bastille Day. As she sauntered through Paris streets, it seemed to Emma the Past walked far too closely at her side. There had stood the guillotine. That road was the one along which the mob escorted back to Paris the carriage containing Louis XVI and his Marie Antoinette. Here stood Napoleon's tomb. History had its place, but should it all but obscure the present?

They journeyed to Versailles and walked through what Emma described as "that shell of royalty." Her imagination brought back to life again the lords and ladies who'd spent days and nights of luxury within these costly walls. The Lazarus sisters thought of going as far as Nice, then decided to return to London.

Back in London, they planned a tour of the British Isles; and in various cities of Ireland and Scotland Emma spoke to important Jews about Jewish colonization in Palestine. The scenic beauty of the countryside enthralled her, and she stored up mental images that could be brought forth again and re-lived to the end of her life. She wrote to New York friends: "I've discovered that almost no pleasure equals the pleasure of travel."

She and her sister sailed for home on September 15th, and six smooth sailing days gave Emma complete relaxation. Again she spent many hours at the ship's railing, looking across the waves, and now she thought of her Portuguese ancestors who must have stood thus upon the deck of a 1497 sailing vessel taking them from cruel persecution. She'd read of them being crowded into ancient ships, some of them spending four terrible months under merciless captains and crews, only to be cast without supplies on Africa's barren coast. She closed her eyes and gave thanks for today, for today's America. For "one nation, under God."

As the ship neared New York Harbor, Emma's heart lifted, as do hearts of all Americans at sight of their loved native land. Had she been addressing her poems too exclusively to "her people" rather than to "the people"? She must change this. From now on, she'd write for all humanity.

At the time of Emma's return from this first visit abroad, September 21, 1883, no Statue of Liberty guarded New York. The statue was still being created in France by Frederic Auguste Bartholdi, the young artist who'd used his mother as model for the goddess with raised right hand holding aloft the torch of enlightenment. Gustave Eiffel, later of Eiffel Tower fame, was designing the statue's steel framework. The statue, a gift from the people of France, would be shipped to the United States in 1885.

Emma had seen models of the statue in Paris, and was aware that the scroll in the left hand of the goddess was the Declaration of Independence. She knew that the statue's costly pedestal would be paid for by public subscription in the United States.

At home again in New York City, she plunged into work. In December of 1883 she received a letter from the Honorable William M. Evarts, Chairman for the American Committee for the Statue of Liberty, asking her for a poem about the statue. She protested that she "could not write to order." But two days later she wrote her famous sonnet: *The New Colossus*. She wrote it for all the people of the world.

The next year, 1884, saw the beginning of the illness that eventually was to take her life. She grew conscious of intense fatigue, but fought it valiantly; and continued to organize groups to discuss the raising of money for a Jewish Fatherland in Palestine. She wrote articles and poems. But extreme fatigue forced her to spend days in bed; and the doctors, failing to diagnose her ailment, merely prescribed a nerve tonic and plenty of sleep.

She was beginning to feel a little better when Moses Lazarus became ill. In her concern for him she forgot her own physical condition, and sat day and night at the bedside of her beloved father who, through all the years had been partner in her every ambition.

On March 9, 1885, Moses Lazarus died. For days afterward, Emma could not believe he had gone. She'd catch herself thinking: "I must tell Father I've finished that poem." Or, "Father will be pleased to see today's sunshine." Suddenly she'd be overwhelmed with the truth that poems or sunshine were no longer of concern to him. Perhaps while going over papers she'd see again his beloved handwriting. And she would dissolve in tears.

For eight weeks after his death, she continued to live in that memory-filled house where every chair and bookshelf spoke his name. And then, on May 15th, Emma and her sister Josephine sailed for Europe.

They spent the summer in England, the autumn in Holland. In Amsterdam Emma visited the art gallery, coming back again and again to stand before Rembrandt's *Night Watch*, or the portrait of the shabby bearded Jew, to whom Rembrandt's brush had given quiet, profound dignity. Rembrandt seemed to be saying to her: "Look, Emma Lazarus. Here, as I see them, are the people of my time." She began an article: "The Genius and Personality of Rembrandt" but did not finish it.

She and Josephine traveled to Italy, spent a month in

Florence, a day in Pisa, then went to Rome. They saw the Vatican and the Sistine Chapel; and in the courtyard of St. Peter's they watched kneeling men and women receive the Pope's blessing.

Emma went alone to the Colosseum and climbed over its ruins. She stood looking up at the tiers and tiers of seats, wondering which seat had been the Emperor's. She visualized the cruel sport enjoyed by 50,000 shouting spectators, and imagined she could smell the lions. She remembered that the Colosseum, like the Pyramids, was built by captured Hebrews.

She and her sister went to Paris, where Emma became very ill and she had to spend months in bed. Finally, her strength gradually returning, she was able to sit up for an hour a day in an easy chair on the balcony of the apartment they had rented. "The world looks beautiful!" she wrote to her sisters in New York. "There is no such cure for pessimism as a severe illness."

At last she was able to take short drives again. She visited the Louvre and, as Heine had done, feasted her eyes upon the beautiful statue of the Venus de Milo. She visited Heine's grave. She wrote: "The day before I visited his tomb, the barrier-wall between the Jewish and Christian portions of the cemetery of Montmartre had been demolished by order of the French Government. As I saw the rubbish and wreck left by the work of human destruction, I could not but reflect with bitterness that the day had not yet dawned beyond the Rhine when Germany, free from race-hatred and bigotry, is worthy and ready to receive her illustrious Semitic son."

On July 23, 1887, she and Josephine sailed for home. As their ship passed the Statue of Liberty in New York Harbor on July 31st, Emma gazed at it through tears of emotion. With what indescribable warmth the statue welcomed the home-coming traveler! Emma had no way of knowing, of course, that in 1903, sixteen years after her death, the statue itself would bear upon its pedestal an inscription of her poem, to be read year after year by admiring millions.

She went from the ship to her home at 18 West Tenth Street, where her sisters put her to bed and gave her tender care. She steadily grew worse and now suffered periods of intense pain that no sedative could subdue. At last doctors were able to diagnose her trouble. Cancer.

Between these attacks of pain, she was almost her old self. She read letters from friends, glanced over her latest book of poems, entitled: *By the Waters of Babylon*, and asked Josephine to play the music of Bach or Beethoven.

When strong enough to sit up against pillows, she'd receive visitors and talk with them of plans for Palestine. Her mind remained clear to the last.

Emma Lazarus died on November 19, 1887. She is buried in the family plot at Cypress Hills Cemetery, in New York City.

Her poetry, her pioneer work in education, her contribution to the cause of a Jewish Homeland in Palestine, all lighted a bright torch in this land of her birth. In ancient Greek relay races the runner, at the end of his lap, handed his torch to his successor. Since Emma's day, her torch has been snatched up by runners hurrying on to great accomplishment. But it might be well to pause now and then and glance back at this valiant girl, a first runner, who in her short thirty-eight years of life out-distanced them all. It might be well to take a second look. And then a third. Lest we forget.

7

MAGGIE LENA WALKER

(1867-1934)

Maggie Lena Walker was born of Negro parents in Richmond, Virginia, not far from St. John's Church in which Patrick Henry asked his famous question: "Is life so dear, is peace so sweet, as to be purchased at the price of slavery?" By the time Maggie Lena entered the world, one war had won freedom for Patrick Henry and his people; another had won freedom for all people in our country, but that second war had dealt Richmond such a blow that only now, the year of her birth, had the city regained consciousness and begun to climb to its feet.

Richmond's Van Lew Mansion was Maggie Lena's birthplace. And Miss Van Lew, daughter of the mansion's owner, had gone to school as a girl in Philadelphia and there learned that slavery was wrong. She'd come home to convince her father of this, and he had freed his fifteen Negro men and women bought long ago, at auction. Among them was the light-colored beautiful Elizabeth Draper, and the handsome young mulatto, William Mitchell. Elizabeth and William, after receiving freedom, stayed on to work for wages. They fell in love and were married. Two years before the birth of their daughter, Maggie Lena, the smudge of slavery had been wiped from the map of the United States.

During the War between the States, Miss Van Lew had been a Northern sympathizer, and daily risked her life to help Union men escape from the Confederate prison, hiding them in her home, and giving secret vital information to officers of the Union Army. Her father had died but she remained in the mansion with her Negro servants; and at war's end, while downtown Richmond burned, she raised the Stars and Stripes over her home.

Little Maggie Lena had permission to wander through the Van Lew mansion, and the library with its thousands of volumes enchanted her. Somehow, perhaps with Miss Van Lew's tutoring, Maggie learned to read at an early age. She was soon reciting poems with such expression and animation that her father, laying a hand on her soft dark hair, would say: "Child, you're a born actress!"

Her father liked to take little Maggie out on the front lawn of the mansion and show her the whole city. Richmond, like Rome, was built on seven hills, and upon the highest hill stood the Van Lew Mansion.

"I watched Richmond burn, standing on this spot," he'd say to the child. "Blocks of stores, factories, warehouses, all went up in dancing flames."

Maggie would nod, but she was thinking of the future, not the past. Soon her father would get the job of head waiter in St. Charles Hotel, and she and her parents would move downtown into a house of their very own.

This came to pass. Maggie's father got the job, and the Mitchells moved into a small house in the Negro section on Thirteenth Street, between Broad Street and Marshall. William made money. And soon a baby boy, Johnny, was born into the family, and life held laughter, good times, love.

Maggie, attending the old Lancaster school, taught by two Southern white women, stood high in her class.

And then one night after he'd finished his hotel work, Maggie's father was hurrying home along a dark street beside the James River, when he was set upon by thieves. After killing him, they tossed his body into the water. Five days later his body was washed ashore.

Maggie would always remember her father's funeral, the heavy perfume of flowers, the sympathetic friends. She remembered walking back to the empty house with her mother and small brother.

Now her mother was head of family and she found the going hard. In that pre-Social Security day, when Life Insurance for Negro families was unknown, when the Government offered no aid to dependent children, Elizabeth Draper Mitchell, Maggie's remarkable mother, vowed that she would keep the home together and *never accept charity*. Thus, a week or so after her husband's death, she began to wash and iron for white families "on the Hill," doing the work in her own kitchen. Maggie had the job of calling for and delivering the laundry.

Maggie would come home from school in the afternoon to find her mother stirring a boiler of clothes on the stove, or bending over a wash tub, or ironing a ruffled dress. The heavy iron handle would have burned the palm of her hand but for the thick pad with which she held it. She'd manage a smile for Maggie, and show her the folded "wash" all ready to be carried out and loaded upon the little wagon.

Taking young Johnny with her for the adventure, Maggie would tug the heavily loaded wagon along Broad Street, and up Richmond's many hills, to the house where the laundry belonged. There her mother's work would be exchanged for a few pennies; and Maggie would pull the wagon to another house for a bundle of soiled clothes and begin the homeward journey, now all down hill. She and young Johnny became a familiar sight on Richmond's streets. Passers-by gave her a friendly smile and nod.

From nine until three, five days a week, school was a happy holiday for Maggie Lena, and learning a pure joy. The teacher lent her books which she'd read in the evening after Johnny was in bed and her mother sat sewing and darning.

Geography fired her imagination and took her to Europe, Asia, Africa. Most exciting of all was Africa, land of her ancestors.

When she'd exhausted her teacher's supply of books dealing with Africa, Maggie went to the library. The librarian became interested in Maggie, and gave her many volumes on African history and geography.

She delved into these with a prospector's fervor. How amazing that Africa, united to Asia by the Suez Canal, separated from Europe by the Mediterranean Sea, should be three times the size of the United States and have a 16,000-mile coast line!

She found the history of the slave trade almost beyond belief. From 1650 to 1850, along Africa's West Coast, rum and firearms had been exchanged for men and women, greedy African tribesmen selling their war-prisoners, captured from other tribes, for these commodities. When their prisoner supply was exhausted, the tribesmen applied midnight torches to sleeping African villages, catching the inhabitants, men and women and children, as they fled from the flames.

The captives, closely packed on slave ships for stormy weeks of sailing, suffered horrors that could not possibly be described. Four out of five captives died, their bodies tossed into the sea. The trip itself proved an endurance test from which only those with great physical fortitude survived. Life was cheap. But even with their four-out-of-five loss in human cargo, the slave trader made 300% on his money invested.

As demand for slaves increased, the interior of Africa was searched for human beings; and during slave-trading years, millions of Africans were torn from their native land to find death on the high seas or to enter slavery throughout the world. More than ten million were sold on American soil.

Maggie discovered that Negroes from various parts of Africa differed greatly from one another. Central Africans, and those from the West Coast, were tall, very dark, very muscular. Southern Africans were light of skin and small of stature. The Berbers, in the North, were brown, with glossy brown hair and European features.

In school, during geography period, Maggie not only became the star of her class, but as far as Africa was concerned, now knew more than did her teacher. One day the teacher asked her to describe the flowers growing along the banks of the Nile River, and when Maggie stood up to answer, the door opened and in walked the Principal. For the Principal's benefit, the teacher repeated her question.

Maggie described the flora of the banks of the Nile, and when she had finished, the Principal asked, with a smile:

"Now, Maggie Lena Walker, just where is Richmond's post office?"

Maggie felt her heart beat quickly, with embarrassment. She didn't exactly know. But she *would* know by this time tomorrow!

"I'm proud of you for learning Africa so well, Maggie," said the Principal, kindly. "But it's far more important to be familiar with your own city's geography and history. If you'll read about Richmond, you'll discover that it has a colorful, dramatic past; and you'll learn that Richmond today is one of the most interesting cities in America."

After that, Richmond's history became one of Maggie's ruling passions, and she began to live in Virginia's proud past. Why, Richmond was only fifty miles from Jamestown. And it was at Jamestown that Captain John Smith had landed in 1607 with 105 cavaliers. A week after the landing, Captain Newport had sailed for six days up the James River and reached a little island near the foot of what is now Ninth Street in Richmond, and had stood upon the island, looking across at what was to be this great city. Captain John Smith had later bought the site of Richmond from Chief Powhatan, father of Pocahontas.

It thrilled her to read that a Major William Mayo had plotted a "city of 32 squares" on Church Hill in 1737. In St. John's Church, on one of those squares, the Second Virginia Convention had convened in 1775; and six years later, when Richmond with a population of 684 had become Virginia's capital, the city was pillaged by Benedict Arnold, but later rescued from the British by the arrival of Lafayette.

As capital of the Confederate States of America, Richmond had endured incredible suffering and hardship between 1861 and 1865. It was then evacuated and burned, but later sprang up from the ruins to become an important center of trade.

Maggie, enriched now by historical lore, would pull her laundry wagon far out of its way while she viewed the important landmarks. She'd pause on Main Street before the house where Edgar Allen Poe had lived with his foster-father, John Allen. She'd walk westward from Twelfth and Broad Streets to the Capitol Building, which had been constructed from plans furnished by Thomas Jefferson after a visit to Nimes, France, where he'd viewed and fallen in love with the original of that charming piece of Roman architecture, with its beautiful columns.

Leaving her wagon against the curb for a moment, Maggie would walk into the Capitol's rotunda to gaze up at a statue of George Washington, the only statue posed for by Washington himself, in life. So *this* was the Father of her Country! She looked up into his strong, kindly face, wanting to tell him how much she appreciated his heroic days at Valley Forge and his great leadership. Thank you, George Washington. *Thank you!*

After her explorations of the past, it was good to come back to the present and walk down her own street toward home. Wonderful to possess a dear mother, a young brother, good friends. What would all the heroes of history give, if only they might enjoy *today?*

It made her sad to realize how hard her mother had to work within their kitchen's whitewashed walls, and she pondered on the cause of her mother's bondage to poverty. Money, of course, would buy her release. With money, her mother would spend no more days over the scrubbing board; someone would be doing *her* laundry! Money bought time, didn't it? And time was life itself.

Of course school, as always, was going well. During noon hour on the school playground, she and her friends sat on a bench beneath a huge sycamore tree and ate lunch. They could not of course foresee that someday, as the men and women of Richmond, they'd take their places in the city's march toward progress. The boy seated near the end of the bench would edit a Richmond newspaper; several of the girls would become teachers, and Maggie herself would grow up to be one of the great women of her race.

On this particular day, Maggie watched a boy eat part of his sandwich and then toss the crust into the trash can. She read him a small lecture on "wilful waste." Another boy, perhaps trying to impress Maggie, perhaps himself impressed by her expressive dark eyes and shining dark hair, quoted a rhyme that all of them had learned in early childhood.

> Wilful waste makes woeful want—
> And you may live to say,
> "I wish I had that little crust
> That once I threw away."

The boys and girls found this very funny. If you saved a crust for two or three months, could you *eat* it? The rhyme didn't make sense.

Maggie explained that perhaps a crust wouldn't "save" too long, but what about a penny? Or a hundred pennies? Or a thousand? Maybe this was what the rhyme meant.

The children thoughtfully agreed. Years later, teaching the crust-of-bread rhyme to their own children, they remembered this scene and Maggie's words.

It was during her High School days that Maggie attended a revival service in the Baptist Church and became "saved." After Baptism, she felt closer to God.

She began to wonder how she could lighten her mother's work, and decided to rise an hour earlier each morning to do the marketing. Basket on arm, she'd walk down to the Old Market where farmers displayed their fruit and meat and vegetables on stands in separate stalls. Gradually, she learned to recognize a bargain.

Walking home with the heavy basket, she inhaled the sweet perfume of magnolias and lilacs. Negresses in colored turbans came out to sweep off porches of fine homes behind high spiked iron fences, and Maggie would glance through the fences at colorful flowerbeds, climbing roses. Richmond *must* be the world's garden spot!

In the business section of town the street cleaners were at work; prisoners in striped uniforms dragging heavy balls and chains as they pushed brooms or lifted rubbish into trash carts. Maggie, searching their faces, tried to read their thoughts. Slavery had been abolished, yet here were men in chains.

A man could be free, yet in slavery to sin, laziness, temptation. She'd never thought of that before. Real freedom lay in being good. If everyone were good, like her mother, courtrooms and jails would close. There'd be no need for police. Think of the money saved!

Her thoughts always turned toward money, didn't they? But money was magic. It was the Fairy Godmother's wand. She saw a poor horse panting as it pulled a wagon up the hill. Money could buy that horse and put him into a green pasture. What was that but magic?

At home her mother was scrubbing sudsy clothes against a washboard in the tub. Maggie asked her mother whether money was magic, and Mrs. Mitchell turned to smile.

"It's good magic or bad magic. Depending on how it's used, Maggie."

Mrs. Mitchell's daughter pondered this.

After graduating from High School, Maggie attended Normal School and became a teacher in the very classroom where, as a child, she had learned long division. Gone were her chores of early marketing, delivering laundry, and the rest. With the "magic" of her teacher's salary she'd given her mother freedom from drudgery. Johnny, who had always disliked school, now worked in a Richmond tobacco factory, but dreamed of going to New York to "make something of himself." He and Maggie lived at home and their mother kept house for them.

Maggie was now a slim, tall, beautiful young woman whose cheerful disposition, infectious laughter and generous nature, made for her many friends. Several young men had already proposed marriage, but Maggie, enjoying each day to the full, wanted nothing changed.

A few years before, she had joined the Independent Order of Saint Luke, an insurance organization formed in Baltimore in 1867 for the purpose of helping the sick and burying the dead. Perhaps its appeal for her had something to do with those well-remembered days of poverty after her dear father's death.

Now she had advanced in the Saint Luke Organization to the position of Right Worthy Grand Chief, and her after-school hours were crowded with such duties as visiting the sick, securing for them competent medical attention, and finding nurses. As the organization was also socially-minded, it sponsored dinners and parties for its members, and Maggie was expected to supervise some of these gatherings.

One evening, at a Saint Luke party, she met handsome young Armstead Walker, who worked for his father, a well known Negro building contractor in Richmond. For the first time in her twenty-three years, she fell deeply in love.

Suddenly she wanted everything changed. Instead of teaching other people's children, she wanted children of her own. Instead of being content to live with her mother and brother, she wanted her own home. She no longer desired complete independence. She wanted to share life, through the years, with Armstead Walker, in an understanding, harmonious partnership.

They were married on September 14, 1890. Maggie gave up teaching and moved with Armstead into the fine large home he'd built for her. He insisted that she must not bury herself in housework and cooking, but should retain her active interest in the Independent Order of Saint Luke. Thus she became a "career wife" as well as a homemaker.

The marriage proved to be a very happy one. Two sons were born to the Armstead Walkers, and Maggie's mother, who lived nearby, delighted in visiting her grandsons daily and spoiling them, in the way of all grandmothers. Fortunately, Maggie had a competent housekeeper and nurse who took household duties from her shoulders and left her free for her Saint Luke duties. To better serve the organization, she enrolled in business college and learned typewriting, shorthand, bookkeeping and business management.

Her father-in-law admired Maggie's ambition and her attitude toward hard work, and enjoyed talking with her. He explained that his building of low-priced houses supplied a need. "Always *supply a need*, Maggie," he told her, "and you'll be a success in business."

Now Maggie was elected to the highest office in the Saint Luke order: Grand Secretary-Treasurer. The title sounded very impressive, but in truth the organization was on the brink of despair, with a debt of $400 and with only $31.61 in the Treasury. The man whom Maggie replaced had refused to continue in office because, he said, the Order "was at a low ebb" and, also, he was "getting poor co-operation from the other officers and the Order was neither growing nor developing." None but a brave woman would have assumed leadership of a bankrupt organization with less than 1,000 members. But bravery was one of Maggie Lena Walker's most outstanding traits; and besides, she was remembering her father-in-law's advice: *supply a need*. Surely there were thousands of men and women who stood in need of just such a Fraternal Order as the Saint Luke!

What were the needs of her people? Insurance, for one thing. By paying a few cents a day to the Order, they could feel financially safe if overtaken by sickness. They needed friends, and friends the Order would offer in generous measure. They needed fun, and here again the Order was useful in organizing parties and social good times.

The Treasury's $31.61 would not do all this, nor was its $400 debt any help. Maggie found it necessary to turn her thoughts toward money-making.

Fortunately she had inherited from some ancestor a great gift; the ability to sway an audience. She could make a speech that held its listeners spellbound. She began to travel from town to town, and to tell large groups of people what her newly organized Saint Luke Fraternity wanted to do for them. She became a teacher again, but now her classroom was the entire State of Virginia. Her listeners joined the Order and worked for it.

By the end of the first year she had paid off the $400 and had several thousand dollars in the Order's Treasury. Three thousand new Councils were formed, each with a membership of thirty or more. "Loyalty to the group must be your first concern," she told the members. She added: "Never ask what you can get from the Organization. Ask *what you can do for it.*"

Daily, she impressed upon members the wisdom of saving money while they were young, strong and healthy. This money, properly invested, would someday work for them.

She was deeply concerned about the young people of her race, and organized Juvenile branches of the Order throughout Virginia. She'd describe to groups of children the street cleaners of Richmond, prisoners dragging ball and chain. She said that certain men and women everywhere, were in bondage to sin, wastefulness and laziness. Be on guard! Earn freedom!

She told the children that the Ten Commandments, the

Lord's Prayer, the Sermon on the Mount, contained in them-selves almost enough truth to live by. But do not lock these learned truths in some mental safe; weave them into daily living; they must "show" in our daily acts of loving kindness, she explained.

Maggie now decided that there was a need for a literary organ, to spread news of the Order's work. In 1902, she established the Saint Luke Herald, later known as the Saint Luke Fraternal Bulletin. Today this newspaper has thousands of subscribers. It contains valuable information on health, thrift, education, home management. It reports the Order's business and gives news of its members. It has never published scandal.

A year after her newspaper was established, Maggie went before the Saint Luke Grand Council and urged the formation of a Savings Bank to serve the members as well as fellow citizens of Richmond. Such a bank would *supply a need*.

In November, 1903, the Saint Luke Penny Savings Bank opened its doors with a paid-up capital of twenty-five thou-sand dollars and deposits of eight thousand. Maggie Lena Walker became President and remained in that capacity for the next twenty-seven years. She was the first woman bank president in the United States, the only one in the history of her race.

During all her years in the president's chair, she was easily accessible to anyone who wanted to talk to her, no matter what his financial status. She looked upon each caller, in her office, as a friend.

Many girls now worked in the bank, and as soon as any girl advanced to a salary of fifty dollars a month, Maggie began to try to talk her into buying a home. The girl was encouraged to save every possible penny, and when she had enough for a first payment on a house, the bank helped her buy it. Hundreds of Negro homes in Richmond were thus financed through the bank's help.

Maggie believed, with Thomas Carlyle, in "doing the duty nearest." One evening, after working late at the bank, Maggie stopped to talk with the scrub woman. Was she saving part of her earnings?

The scrub woman, pausing in her work, looked up into the president's kindly face. She said: "Ma'm, I'm earning only five dollars a week."

"Could you save fifty cents a week?" asked Mrs. Walker. "In a year that would amount to twenty-six dollars."

The scrub woman admitted she could do a lot with twenty-six dollars. If she had it.

"You could do a lot right now," Maggie told her. "You could go to business college part time. Ever thought of that? You could thus fit yourself for a better job."

The woman hadn't thought of it. But with Maggie's help she saved and went to school and studied. When she finished business school, she was given a bank job. Not doing manual labor. At a desk.

Eighteen years from the night Maggie stopped to speak to her, this woman held the position of head bookkeeper in the Saint Luke Bank. She had a fair-sized savings account. She owned a comfortable home.

At the corner of Second and Clay Streets in Richmond, a one-legged bootblack had rented a chair with no canopy against the wind and weather. Mrs. Walker frequently passed his stand; one day she noticed him leaning against his chair in the rain, a dejected business man, without customers. She spoke to him. How much money did he save each week? Would he care to join the Saint Luke Order?

He joined the Order, and Maggie took a personal interest in sending him customers and watching his small savings

grow. When he had fifty dollars in the bank, she helped him
rent a little place of his own with three chairs. Seven years
later he had a shop with twelve chairs; had bought a home
for his mother, furnished it, and was free of debt. He had a
bank balance of five hundred dollars.

Maggie, always deeply concerned with the welfare of children, encouraged the Saint Luke children to sell papers, cut
grass, do chores, run errands, and save, save, save. She tried
to give them a sense of moral responsibility for the wise use
of money. Thrift was not an end in itself. Money was valuable
for what it did for one's own growth and development. And
the most important thing money could buy for a girl or boy
was education.

She now thought of an idea that has since been used in
thousands of School Savings Bank projects throughout the
country. She gave each child a little cardboard bank, and
encouraged him to drop his pennies into it. As soon as he
(or she) had a dollar, the cardboard bank must be brought to
the Big Bank, and this would start a savings account just
like mother's or father's.

The idea flourished and soon thousands of Richmond children were dropping every available penny into cardboard
banks, and shaking them to hear the joyous jingle. How many
children were thus started on the road to a better way of life,
a better education, has never been recorded. But millions of
today's adults, the country over, can remember the little
cardboard banks, given by the Big Bank and thus can trace
their first steps in thrift to an idea conceived by Maggie Lena
Walker.

She now began to concentrate upon the problem of worthy
and intelligent young people whose families could not afford
to give them a college education. The bank was not a paternal
institution, yet a way should be found to lend college money

to these boys and girls if they would sign a note promising to repay the money once they possessed a college degree and a good job.

She went to the Insurance Department of her Independent Order of Saint Luke and asked for an Education Fund to be used for this purpose. Her request was granted, but she waited until the Fund reached the amount of ten thousand dollars before she made use of it.

Then girls and boys who had been Saint Luke members for three years, whose former teachers recommended them, and who had adequate credentials for college entrance, were encouraged to borrow enough money to see them through four college years. Of course they were expected to find odd jobs too, and to borrow no more than was absolutely necessary. And they were asked to sign an agreement to repay the money with interest, as soon as they could, after graduation.

The plan was a great success. Every student, without exception, repaid the borrowed money after obtaining a degree and finding a job; and thus the original ten thousand dollars became an endless chain of helpfulness. The obligation to repay the debt drove home to the students an important truth that Maggie Lena Walker wanted every young man and woman to adopt as his or her philosophy of life: *one should not take without giving value received.*

In the meanwhile Maggie's two sons had grown to manhood, married, and had children of their own. Her brother, Johnny, had died. An accident took the life of her husband, and she lost by death her beloved mother and eldest son. Through all these personal tragedies, she carried on at the bank and continued to build up the Saint Luke Organization, which now had a four-story building of its own in Richmond. The Saint Luke Penny Savings Bank, later called the Con-

solidated Bank and Trust Company, was now located in a
fine new building, too.

Maggie had begun to put on weight, but as she was tall
and wore good clothes, and was always well-corseted, the
added weight seemed to lend her an air of authority. Her own
people in Richmond now watched for her coming and going
and seemed to feel better for a glimpse of this woman whose
life had been one of service. They sent her gifts, not because
she needed them, but because it did their hearts good to try
to tell her, through the gift, that she had their love and
appreciation.

The Saint Luke Organization now had branches in almost
every State in the Union. Millions of dollars had been paid in
death claims, and membership had grown from the original
one thousand, when Maggie Walker accepted its leadership,
to many, many thousands of men and women.

Maggie shared the large house where she lived with all
members of her family: her son and his wife; the wife of her
elder son who had died, and several grandchildren. The children were ever a source of joy to her, and she supervised
their spending and their saving with the greatest care.

The grandchildren were not "given" weekly allowances.
They earned the money by sweeping down the back stairs,
weeding the lawn, trimming the rose bushes. For all these
chores they were well paid, but they received no money at
all unless the work was done to Grandmother Walker's complete satisfaction.

One of Maggie Lena's granddaughters is now a medical
doctor in Chicago. And Dr. Maggie Laura Walker distinctly
remembers that, as a child, she craved a pair of ballet slippers.
Her mother declared that Maggie Laura did not need the
slippers and refused to buy them. Well, would Grandmother
let her have the money, please? Grandmother Walker agreed

to buy the slippers, but Maggie Laura must, of course, pay the money back. It was a loan, not a gift.

And so Maggie Laura learned about loans. It required many weeks of sweeping down the back stairs to pay for the slippers, but Grandmother Walker unsmilingly expected weekly payment. A gift was one thing. A loan was another. Once you borrowed money, it must be repaid. You did not want, you would not accept, "something for nothing."

As the years went by, Mrs. Walker's interests expanded to include many local projects such as the Negro Sanatorium at Burkeville, Virginia, the Manual Training School for Boys at Hanover, the Old Folks' Home in Richmond, and so on. She was appointed trustee for the Frederick Douglas Home in Washington, D. C., as well as director of the National Training School for Girls in Lincoln Heights.

One of her favorite projects was the Industrial School for Delinquent Negro Girls at Peaks, Virginia. Before this school opened, there had been no place for Negro girls arrested for some slight offense except the Richmond Jail. But at this efficiently run Industrial School the life of every girl who entered was transformed.

Each new girl was given a bath, clean clothes, a clean bed, and an absolutely spotless record. All her past sins were "confessed" and then forgiven. She was assigned to a cottage with a housemother and an older girl inmate became her "Big Sister" who offered not only advice in every new situation, but love, too. The girl learned a trade or skill by which she might later earn a living. While at school she enjoyed picnics, trips, picture shows. She learned to play games, to dance and to swim. After two years, she was ready for the world again, prepared physically, educationally and morally to face almost any challenge life offered.

Maggie Walker, as honored member of the Board of

Management, took a personal interest in the individual girls, and often helped them to find jobs on their release. She would speak briefly to them in their classrooms, usually leaving with the admonition: "Carry on! Let us measure up!"

On Sunday, November 30, 1924, five thousand people filled Richmond's Auditorium to celebrate Maggie Lena Walker's twenty-fifth year as Leader of the Independent Order of Saint Luke. Mrs. Walker was showered with praise and with gifts. As one speaker said: "Here is a Prophet who *has* found honor in her own country."

A few months after this, Mrs. Walker was stricken with a form of paralysis that affected her legs. She was fitted with steel braces, and forced to use a wheel chair. This, however, did not lessen her ardor for work. She had a ramp built from the front door of her house to the sidewalk, and a special ramp fastened to her automobile and a seat in the car removed, so that she could be wheeled in her chair from the house into the car beside the driver. At the bank she was wheeled to her own office, and there conducted the business of the day, as usual.

At home, her grandchildren now spent more time at her side, telling her their joys and troubles, giving her glimpses of their world. If the granddaughters went to a party, they always came to Grandmother's bedroom afterward, no matter how late the hour, and told her all about the decorations, refreshments, music, guests.

The grandchildren, knowing that she loved flowers and music, saw to it that fresh flowers were in her room every day, and that she had available at all times the recordings of her favorite artists. They knew that she loved plenty of light in her home in the evenings, and made sure that her large house was brilliantly lighted. Light was her major extravagance.

Two days before she died she went to work at the bank. It had been raining unusually hard and the James River was threatening to overflow, but inside her office that morning everything was neatly in place and the bank itself wore its usual just-scrubbed look. Officials came in to speak to Maggie Lena Walker and to receive her smile.

Hawthorne wrote: "We make the weather." And it was true that Maggie Lena Walker, by her cheerful outlook, created bright days for the hundreds of people who worked for her. She always kept her papers and files in immaculate order, knowing that if she went out of office, never to return, work would go on uninterrupted.

At noon on her last day at the bank, she asked her driver to take her up Church Hill. The Van Lew mansion had disappeared, and now in 1934 there stood, in the mansion's place, a school. She asked the driver to park near the school for a moment, so that she might look down the hill upon Richmond.

Oh, the changes time had wrought! Gone the little girl, herself, tugging the bundle of clothes upon a wagon. Gone were the sweating horses, and in their place were shining cars taking the hill with effortless ease.

Maggie Lena Walker's entire life had been adjustment to change, one change after another. And she'd loved it. She could still feel the thrill of her first ride in an automobile, hearing her first radio broadcast, taking her first airplane trip. She had heard someone say that all these: the automobile, radio, airplane, had been here on earth in Moses' time, waiting to be invented or discovered. Yes, perhaps so. And what "miracles" still lay undiscovered, uninvented?

The day was December 13, 1934. Maggie hadn't made out her Christmas list as yet. She must do this tomorrow. She looked down again at her beloved Richmond, where she'd spent her entire sixty-seven years of life. Suddenly she felt a little tired. She asked the driver to take her home.

On December 14th she remained at home. And on the next day, December 15, 1934, she suffered a heart attack and died.

Among her treasures, a personal letter was found after her death. It was written to her by Mrs. Franklin D. Roosevelt, wife of the President of the United States. The letter said: "I cannot imagine anything more satisfying than a life of the kind of accomplishments which you have had. I congratulate you."

Maggie Lena Walker's life was indeed one of accomplishment. She won success entirely by her own efforts, among her own race. A self-made woman. A great American.